E-01-181

E-01-181

Scott Foresman
Reading
Picture This!

Picture This!

From Past to Present

Are We There Yet?

Imagination.kids

Scott Foresman

About the Cover Artist
As a child, Daniel Craig was crazy about dinosaurs, but in his Minneapolis home, his only pets are his cats, Isaac and Noah, and Winston, a dog. His pets often appear in his paintings.

ISBN 0-673-59644-3

8 9 10-VH-06 05 04 03 02 01

Scott Foresman Reading
Picture This!

Program Authors

Peter Afflerbach

James Beers

Camille Blachowicz

Candy Dawson Boyd

Deborah Diffily

Dolores Gaunty-Porter

Violet Harris

Donald Leu

Susan McClanahan

Dianne Monson

Bertha Pérez

Sam Sebesta

Karen Kring Wixson

Scott Foresman

Editorial Offices: Glenview, Illinois • New York, New York
Sales Offices: Reading, Massachusetts • Duluth, Georgia • Glenview, Illinois
Carrollton, Texas • Menlo Park, California

Contents

FROM PAST
TO PRESENT

Unit 4

Contents

Are We There Yet?

Unit 5

Contents

Unit 6

9

FROM PAST
— TO —
PRESENT

How can our
traditions and the
traditions of others
make our lives
more interesting?

Theme

- A **theme** of a story is a big idea of the story.

- When you read a story, think about what the writer wants you to learn or understand from the story.

- You can use something from your own life to help you understand this theme or big idea.

Read "The Coyote and the Goat" from *Doctor Coyote* by John Bierhorst.

Talk About It

1. The theme of this story is stated in the last sentence. What do you think it means?

2. Another theme of this story might be *Look before you leap*. What from your own life helps you understand what this means?

The Coyote and the Goat

a Native American Aesop's Fable retold by John Bierhorst

Traveling along, Coyote met White Beard, and the two of them traveled together.

When Coyote and White Beard got thirsty, they jumped into a well. They drank their fill; then White Beard began looking around to see how he could get back out.

"Don't worry," said Coyote. "I know how we can do it. Just stand up straight and put your hands against the side of the well. Lift your head so your horns stick out behind, and I'll climb on your back. As soon as I'm out, I'll reach over and pull you up."

It sounded good to White Beard. He did what he was told, and Coyote climbed on top of him. But then, when Coyote was free, he ran around the edge of the well, laughing at White Beard. White Beard was furious.

"Friend," said Coyote, "if your brain was as big as your beard, you would have thought about how to get out before you jumped in."

The truth hits hardest when it's too late to complain.

LOOK AHEAD TO

Ananse's Feast

In the next story, find out the big idea behind why a spider and a turtle trick each other.

Vocabulary

Words to Know

brilliant   greedy feast
delighted guest   stomach

Many words have more than one meaning. To decide which meaning is being used, look for clues in the sentence or paragraph around it.

Read the paragraph below. Pay attention to its meaning as a whole. Does *brilliant* mean "having great ability" or "sparkling"?

A Guest with Bad Manners!

Polly Peacock set the table for a feast. She put out food and cleaned the silverware until it was shining and brilliant. Polly was delighted to see her first dinner guest, Spinner the Spider. At least she was happy until she saw how greedy Spinner was. He ate and ate until his stomach was full and most of the food was gone. Next time, Polly would have her party when Spinner was on vacation!

Write About It

Write an invitation for Polly's next dinner party. Use as many vocabulary words as you can.

14

Ananse's Feast

An Ashanti Tale

retold by Tololwa M. Mollel • illustrated by Andrew Glass

The earth was hot and barren and no one had much to eat except Ananse the Spider. Before the drought clever Ananse had stored away food from his farm, and now he decided to treat himself to a feast.

Ananse shut his door and windows and sealed all the cracks in the walls of his old hut.

"I don't want the delicious smell of my cooking to bring hungry visitors," he muttered.

But somehow the aroma of food escaped and reached Akye the Turtle, who was searching for something to eat on a dusty riverbed nearby.

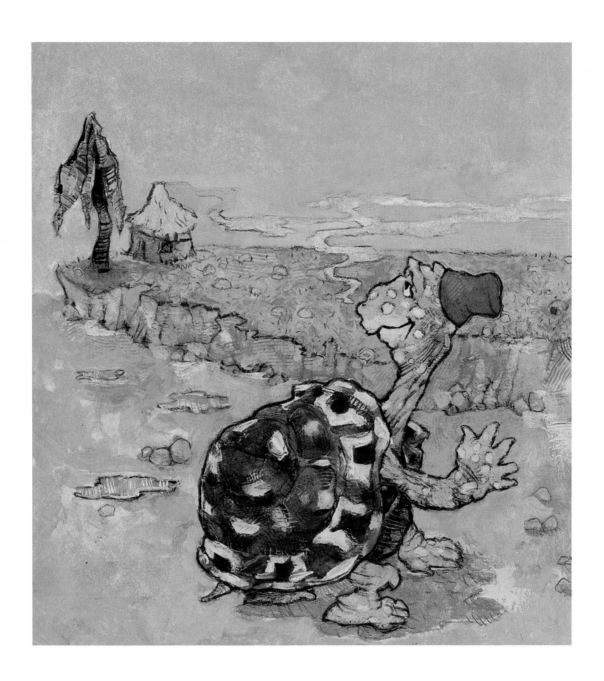

"I'll drop in on my old friend Ananse," thought hungry Akye. "I'm sure he'll spare me a bite."

Ananse was setting the table when he heard a knock on the door. He stood still and listened. "Whoever it is will soon go away," he thought hopefully.

The knocking didn't stop, however, and Ananse had to open the door. He didn't want to share his feast with anyone. Yet when he saw his friend Akye, he couldn't bring himself to send him away.

"Oh, it is you, Akye," said Ananse, smiling. "Come in and be my guest!"

Akye stared at the mountain of food. He didn't know where to start. "I'll eat the golden, crisp fried plantain first," he thought. "How delicious it looks! Oh, look at the steaming hot soft yam and the pepper soup. No, I'll start on the fluffy coconut rice and the creamy beans with ground peanuts."

He was reaching for the rice when Ananse
stopped him. "Your hands are dirty!" he told Akye.
"In my house, it is only good manners to wash
your hands before eating."

Akye looked at his hands, dusty and dirty from his manner of walking on all fours. "Can I have some water to wash them?" he asked.

"I'm sorry, I've used up all the water," replied Ananse. "You must go and wash your hands at the river."

The river was dry except for a few puddles. Akye washed his hands thoroughly in one of them. And back he crawled,

a-kye-kye-die
a-kye-kye-die,

his empty stomach moaning, *Oyei-yaai oyei-yaai!* as he thought of the fluffy coconut rice and the creamy beans with ground peanuts.

But greedy Ananse had eaten up the rice and the beans.

"No matter," thought Akye, "I'll have the steaming hot soft yam and the pepper—"

"Look, your hands, you didn't wash them," Ananse said, with a frown.

Akye looked at his dusty hands and shook his head. "Strange—I did wash them. Well, I'll go and wash them again."

At the river Akye rubbed, scrubbed, rinsed, and wiped his hands. Then up the riverbank he clambered,

> *a-kye-kye-die*
> *a-kye-kye-die,*

his empty stomach groaning, *Oyei-yai-yaai oyei-yai-yaai!* as he thought of the steaming hot soft yam and the pepper soup.

He got back to find selfish Ananse finishing up the yam and the soup.

"Your hands are still dirty!" mumbled Ananse.

"But I just washed them!" protested Akye.

"You don't seem to have done a good job of it," replied Ananse, laughing. "Go back to the river!"

By the time Akye returned from the river,
cunning Ananse had eaten all the food and was
wearing a big satisfied grin.

Akye suddenly realized how Ananse had tricked
him. He only smiled, however, and said to well-fed
Ananse, "Thank you for inviting me to the feast.
I hope one day I can repay you."

A few days later, the drought ended. Rain came
down. The earth bloomed and food crops burst
forth. Rivers flowed, teeming with fish and crabs.

It rained so much that farms became swampy.
The harvest was late, and Ananse, who was not
a good fisherman, had little to eat. So he was
delighted to receive an invitation to a feast at
the turtle's home under the river.

Hungry Ananse arrived at the river dressed for
the feast in a brilliant ceremonial robe. He climbed
up a tall tree on the riverbank.

Then, straight as an arrow, he dived into
the water.

Bul bul bul bul bul, he sank.

He was too light to stay underwater, though.
And *bul bul bul bul bul*, he rose, floating
back to the surface.
He climbed higher on the tree and dived again.
Bul bul bul bul bul, he sank.
Bul bul bul bul bul, he rose.

Then Ananse had an idea. "I know how I can get to the feast!" he exclaimed. He filled the enormous pockets of his robe with pebbles from the beach. Then he climbed to the very top of the tree and came streaking down.

Bul bul bul bul bul, he sank.

Bul bul bul bul bul, he sank.

Down to the feast!

Akye was seated at a table laden with plump mounds of juicy, tender crabmeat, dressed in a brilliant ceremonial robe of his own. With his heavy shell, he had no trouble staying down.

The turtle noticed the bulging weight of pebbles in Ananse's pockets and touched the spider's robe admiringly.

"What a beautiful robe!" he said, and smiled. "But I suggest you take it off before we eat."

"What!" cried Ananse.

"In my house," Akye said sweetly, "it is only good manners to take off your robe before eating." And he began to slip out of his own robe.

Ananse couldn't let Akye think he was an ill-mannered guest. Reluctantly, he took off his robe. And although he tried hard to cling to the table . . .

Bul bul bul bul bul, he rose.

Bul bul bul bul bul, he rose.

Back to the surface!

Unable to return to the feast without his heavy robe, Ananse sat shivering on the bank, his empty stomach wailing,

Oyei-yai-yai-yaai!

Oyei-yai-yai-yaai!

as he thought of the plump mounds of juicy, tender crabmeat.

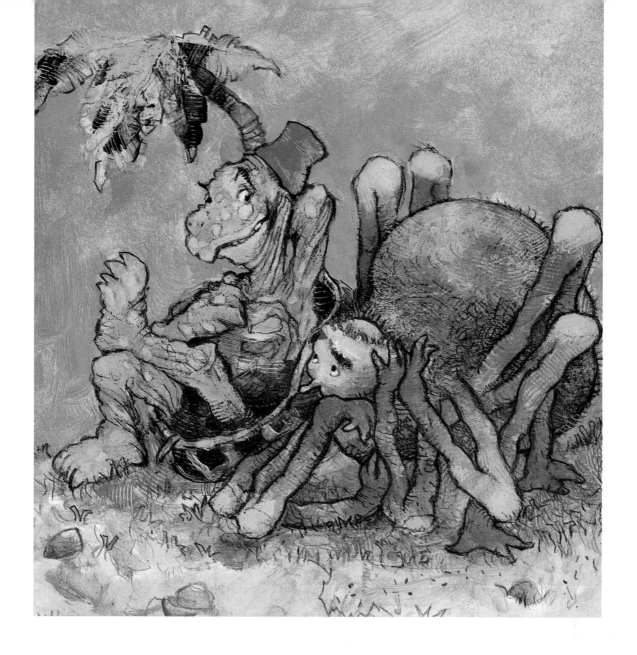

Some time later, well-fed Akye walked out
the river,

a-kye-kye-die
a-kye-kye-die.

With a big satisfied grin, he came to squat
alongside his old friend Ananse.

"What a delicious feast that was," said Akye,
rubbing his full belly with pleasure. "Thank you
so much for coming. The meal would not have
been the same without you. Let's make sure we
have another feast soon!"

About the Author
Tololwa M. Mollel

Tololwa M. Mollel grew up in Tanzania, a country in East Africa. He lived with his grandparents, who were storytellers. He not only loved hearing their stories, he loved to read other people's stories—and to write his own. "I wrote about pirates, magical lamps, knights, and detectives at various stages of my school years," he says.

When Mr. Mollel went to college in Canada, he kept writing for fun. After he married and had a child, he decided that he wanted to write for children. What would he write about? Since he knew so many African folk tales from his childhood, he decided to use a story that had been told to him by his grandfather. Mr. Mollel called it *The Orphan Boy*. In this Masai folk tale, a boy learns about secrets, trust, and betrayal. Mr. Mollel has retold other folk tales from different parts of Africa. His stories often have a lesson about life in them.

"Writing for children for me is both challenging and rewarding," he says. "It is challenging to put complicated ideas into simple terms. It is rewarding when children enjoy the stories."

Open for Discussion

People tell this tale to their children. Why do you think they do?

Comprehension Check

1. Which character is more clever—Ananse or Akye? Give examples from the story to support your answer.

2. Think of two or three words to describe Ananse. Find parts of the story that support your choices.

3. Will Ananse and Akye ever have another meal together? Why or why not?

4. What is one big idea, or **theme,** in *Ananse's Feast*?

5. In what way can this **theme** help you in your life?

What's Cooking?

Ananse and Akye prepared feasts of foods from Africa. What would you serve at a feast? Think about what you eat at family celebrations or on holidays. Write a menu of favorite feast foods.

The Fox and the Stork

retold by Suzanne I. Barchers

Props

Consider having various dishes, including a shallow dish and jar, on the side of the stage. This adds to the setting without giving away the story. To act out the script more fully, you could add large handkerchiefs or dinner napkins as bibs.

Characters

Narrator
Fox
Stork

Reading Across Texts

Reading a Fable

✓ **Look for a brief story.** A fable has a beginning, middle, and end.

✓ **Look for animal characters.** Characters in a fable are often animals.

✓ **Look for a lesson.** The lesson, or moral, is the big idea of the fable. It is usually stated at the end of the story.

Focus Your Reading

This fable teaches a lesson about how to treat others. As you read, think about the lesson Ananse learned from Akye.

Narrator: There was a time when the fox and the stork were very good friends. They enjoyed talking about their days. One day they decided to share a meal together.

Fox: Why don't you come to dinner, my good friend? I'll fix my best soup!

Stork: That sounds fine! When shall I come?

Fox: Tonight would be fine for me.

Narrator: That night, the stork was happy just thinking about a bowl of good soup. She even arrived a little early at the fox's den.

Fox: Hello, my friend. Let's waste no time. The soup is ready.

Narrator: But the stork had quite a surprise. The soup was in a shallow bowl. She couldn't eat any of it with her long beak.

Stork: My beak is much too long to be able to eat from that bowl, Fox.

Fox: I *am* sorry that you don't like my soup.

Narrator: And so the stork went home hungry. But the next day she invited the fox to dinner.

Stork: Fox, let's forget that I went home hungry last night. Why don't you come to my home for dinner tonight?

Fox: It would be my pleasure.

Narrator: That night the fox showed up at the stork's home, eager for another meal.

Stork: Welcome, welcome, dear friend. I knew you liked soup, so I made *my* favorite for our meal.

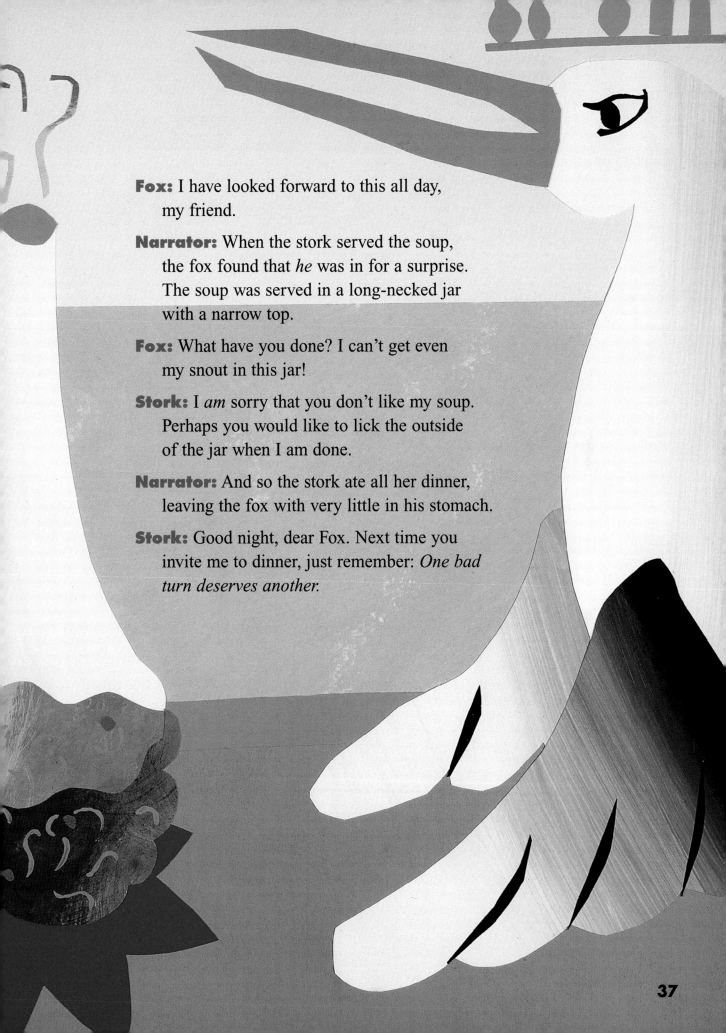

Fox: I have looked forward to this all day, my friend.

Narrator: When the stork served the soup, the fox found that *he* was in for a surprise. The soup was served in a long-necked jar with a narrow top.

Fox: What have you done? I can't get even my snout in this jar!

Stork: I *am* sorry that you don't like my soup. Perhaps you would like to lick the outside of the jar when I am done.

Narrator: And so the stork ate all her dinner, leaving the fox with very little in his stomach.

Stork: Good night, dear Fox. Next time you invite me to dinner, just remember: *One bad turn deserves another.*

Skill Lesson

Setting

- The **setting** is the time and place in which a story happens.

- Look for details or clues that tell you when and where a story takes place.

- Understanding the setting can sometimes help you understand a character's actions.

Read "A Hike with Dad" from *The Lost Lake* by Allen Say.

Write About It

1. Make a list of the words that help you see the setting in "A Hike with Dad."

2. Pretend you are with Dad too. Write a diary entry describing the setting. Share your diary entry with a classmate.

A Hike with Dad
by Allen Say

We started early in the morning. When the fog cleared we saw other hikers ahead of us. Sure enough, Dad became very glum.

"We're going cross-country, partner," he said.

"Won't we get lost?"

"A wise man never leaves home without his compass."

So we went off the trail. The hills went on and on. The mountains went on and on. It was kind of lonesome. It seemed as if Dad and I were the only people left in the world.

And then we hiked into a big forest.

At noontime we stopped by a creek and ate lunch and drank ice-cold water straight from the stream. I threw rocks in the water and fish, like shadows, darted in pools.

"Isn't this a good place to camp, Dad?"

"I thought we were looking for our lake."

"Yes, right . . ." I mumbled.

The forest went on and on.

"I don't mean to scare you, son," Dad said. "But we're in bear country. We don't want to surprise them so we have to make a lot of noise. If they hear us, they'll just go away."

What a time to tell me! I started to shout as loudly as I could. Even Dad wouldn't be able to beat off bears. I thought about those people having fun back at the lake. I thought about the creek, too, with all those fish in it. That would have been a fine place to camp.

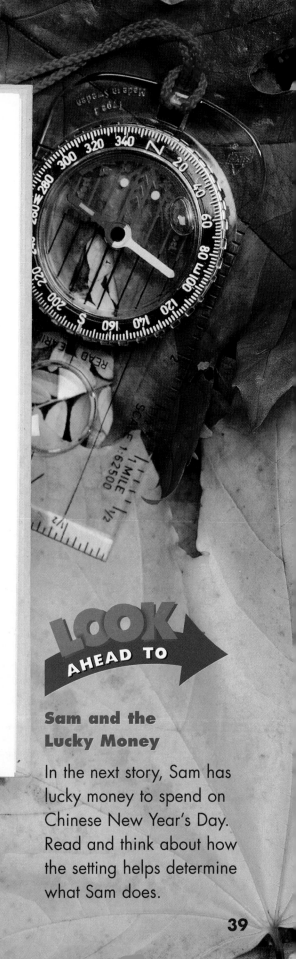

LOOK
AHEAD TO

Sam and the Lucky Money

In the next story, Sam has lucky money to spend on Chinese New Year's Day. Read and think about how the setting helps determine what Sam does.

Vocabulary

Words to Know

appreciate   rustling   scolded
dragon   lucky   startled

When you read, you may come across a word you don't know. To figure out the unfamiliar word, look for clues around it. A clue might be found in an explanation given before or after the unknown word.

Read the paragraph below. Notice how an explanation of *lucky* helps you understand what it means.

The Perfect Present

"I need a gift Grandma can <u>appreciate</u>," Felicia said. She <u>scolded</u> herself for spending her money on candy. A noise <u>startled</u> her—Grandpa! He said, "Here's my <u>lucky</u> coin. Touch it for good fortune." There was a soft <u>rustling</u> as Grandpa took the coin from his pocket. On it was a picture of a <u>dragon</u>. An idea came to her as Felicia touched the coin. She'd write Grandma a story!

Write About It

What story could Felicia tell? Use vocabulary words to write her story.

Sam and the Lucky Money

by Karen Chinn
illustrated by Cornelius Van Wright
and Ying-Hwa Hu

Sam could hardly wait to get going. He zipped up his jacket and patted his pockets. It was time to go to Chinatown for New Year's Day!

Sam thought about sweet oranges and "lucky money": Crisp dollar bills tucked in small red envelopes called *leisees*.

Sam's grandparents gave him leisees every New Year. Each envelope was decorated with a symbol of luck: Two golden mandarins. A Chinese junk. A slithering dragon. A giant peach. Sam's leisees were embossed in gold.

Sam counted out four dollars. Boy, did he feel rich! His parents said he didn't have to buy a notebook or socks as usual. This year he could spend his lucky money *his* way.

"Sam!" his mother called. "It's time to go shopping. Hurry, so we don't miss the lion!"

"Coming!" said Sam.

The streets hummed with the thump of drums and the clang of cymbals. Everywhere dusty red smoke hung in the air left by exploding firecrackers.

"Give me your hand," said his mother. "I don't want you to get lost." Sam took her hand reluctantly. It seemed like everyone was shopping for New Year's meals. There were so many people crowded around the overflowing vegetable bins that Sam had to look out for elbows and shopping bags.

Right next to the vegetable stand were two huge red-paper mounds. Sam kicked the piles with his right foot, and then with his left foot, until he created a small blizzard. On his third kick he felt his foot land on something strange.

"Aiya!" someone cried out in pain.

Startled, he looked up to find an old man sitting against the wall. The stranger was rubbing his foot. *Bare feet in winter!* Sam thought. *Where are his shoes?*

Sam stared at the man's dirty clothes as he backed away. He found his mother picking out oranges and he tugged on her sleeve, pulling harder than he meant to.

"Hey, I need this arm," she said. "Where have you been? It's time to go."

For once, Sam was glad to follow his mother.

In the bakery window, Sam eyed a gleaming row of fresh *char siu bao*, his favorite honey-topped buns. When they opened the door, the smell of sweet egg tarts and coconut pastries erased any thought of the stranger. Sam wondered how many sweets he could buy with four dollars.

"*Nay yu mat yeh ah?*" said a young woman from behind the counter. When Sam gave her a puzzled look, she repeated the question in English. "What do you want?"

Sam was about to ask for buns when he noticed a tray full of New Year's cookies. They were shaped like fish, with fat, pleated tails that looked like little toes. He couldn't help but think about the old man again. Sam decided he wasn't hungry after all. Suddenly, he heard a noise from outside that sounded like a thousand leaves rustling. He ran to the window to see what was happening.

"Look!" he yelled. Bundles of firecrackers were exploding in the street. Rounding the corner was the festival lion, followed by a band of cymbals and drums. Sam pulled his mother outside.

The colorful lion wove down the street like a giant centipede. Teased by a clown wearing a round mask, it tossed its head up and down.

It came to a halt in front of a meat market, and sniffed a giant leisee that hung in the doorway, along with a bouquet of lettuce leaves. With loud fanfare, the band urged the lion toward its prize.

"Take the food! Take the money! Bring us good luck for the New Year!" Sam shouted along with the others. His heart pounded in time with the drum's beat. With a sudden lunge, the lion devoured the leisee all in an eye-blink and continued down the street. The crowd clapped and then quickly dispersed.

"That was a hungry lion," Sam's mother joked. Now he felt hungry too, and wanted to go back to the bakery.

But just then, a large "Grand Opening" sign caught Sam's eye. In the window were cars, planes, robots, and stuffed animals. A new toy store! Just the place to spend his lucky money!

Sam ran down one aisle, then another. He examined a police car with a wailing siren and flashing lights. He squeezed a talking pig and laughed at its loud "Oink, oink!" Then, he spotted the basketballs.

A new basketball was the perfect way to spend his lucky money. But when he saw the price tag, he got angry.

"I only have four dollars," he shouted. "I can't buy this." In fact, everything he touched cost more than that.

"What is four dollars good for?" he complained, stamping his feet. His mother scrunched up her eyes, the way she always did when she scolded him, and guided him out the door.

Sam couldn't help it. Even with all the shiny gold on them, the leisees seemed worthless.

"Sam, when someone gives you something, you should appreciate it," his mother said as she marched him along. Sam stuffed his leisees back in his pockets. The sun had disappeared behind some clouds, and he was starting to feel the chill. He dragged his feet along the sidewalk.

Suddenly, Sam saw a pair of bare feet, and instantly recognized them. They belonged to the old man he had seen earlier. The man also remembered him, and smiled. Sam froze in his steps, staring at the man's feet.

His mother kept walking. When she turned back to check on Sam, she noticed the old man. "Oh," she said, shifting her shopping bags so she could dig in her purse for some coins. "Sorry—I only have a quarter." The man bowed his head several times in thanks.

He acts like it's a million bucks, Sam thought, shaking his head. As they started to walk away, Sam looked down at his own feet, warm and dry in his boots. Suddenly he stopped.

"Can I really do anything I want with my lucky money?" he asked.

"Yes, of course," his mother answered.

Sam pulled his leisees from his pockets. The golden dragon looked shinier than ever. He ran back and thrust his lucky money into the surprised man's hands.

"You can't buy shoes with this," he told the man, "but I know you can buy some socks." The stranger laughed, and so did Sam's mother.

Sam walked back to his mother and took her warm hand. She smiled and gave a gentle squeeze. And as they headed home for more New Year's celebration, Sam knew he was the lucky one.

About the Author
Karen Chinn

Karen Chinn likes to write stories that bring different cultures together. When Karen Chinn was growing up in Seattle, Washington, there weren't many books about Asian Americans in modern settings. She wrote *Sam and the Lucky Money* to celebrate Asian American culture. "I wanted to capture some of the rituals and customs of Chinese New Year's, as well as the excitement of it," she has said. Mrs. Chinn and her husband currently live in Seattle with their daughter.

About the Illustrators
Cornelius Van Wright and Ying-Hwa Hu

Cornelius Van Wright and Ying-Hwa Hu have worked as a team to illustrate two other award-winning books, *Zora Hurston and the Chinaberry Tree* and *A House by the River*. They used watercolors to paint the pictures for these books, as well as for *Sam and the Lucky Money*.

Reader Response

Open for Discussion

If you met Sam, what would you ask him about himself and where he lives?

Comprehension Check

1. Did Sam do the right thing when he gave his money to the man? Tell why you think as you do.

2. Sam's mood changes often in this story. Choose a page and tell what his mood is. Tell why he feels as he does.

3. What do you think Sam will do with his leisees next New Year? Why?

4. What is the **setting** of *Sam and the Lucky Money?*

5. How would the story be different if the **setting** were in a hot place or during the summer?

When Sam Gets Home

In a group, imagine what will happen when Sam tells his grandparents what he did with his leisees. What would Sam say? What would the grandparents say? What would they all do? Act out the scene for classmates.

Cause and Effect

- A **cause** is why something happens.

- An **effect** is what happens.

- Sometimes an author uses clue words, such as *so* and *because,* to tell what happens and why.

- When clue words are not present to signal cause and effect, look for what happens. Stop and think why it happens.

Read "Fire!" by Caroline Evans from *Ranger Rick* magazine.

by Caroline Evans

Talk About It

1. What happened to the pine tree? Why?

2. What effects might the forest fire have on camping and hiking in the forest?

Imagine a hot summer day in a forest in the western United States. A mighty thunderstorm turns the blue sky black. Zap! A bolt of lightning streaks toward the ground and strikes the top of a tall pine tree. Electric current zips down through its trunk and roots. In an instant, the pine tree explodes into a flaming torch.

The burning branches pop and scatter onto the forest floor. Fire spreads to dry twigs and needles. Flames dance over dead logs and leap up nearby tree

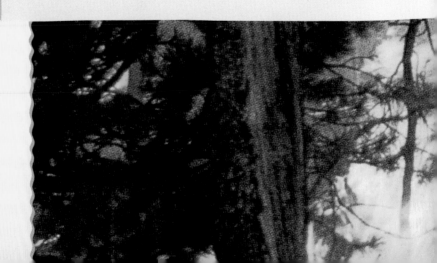

trunks. Soon the forest crackles and snaps in a red-orange light.

This is the end of the forest, right? Actually, the answer is bigger than that. A fire can be just another step in the forest's ongoing natural cycle.

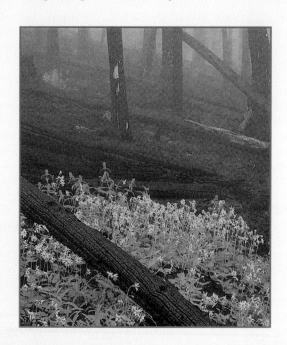

LOOK AHEAD TO

Thunder Cake

In the next story, a young girl is afraid of thunder. Read and find out the effects of her grandmother's cure.

Vocabulary

Words to Know

distance   thunder   lightning
measured   weather   recipe

As you read, you may come across a word you don't know. To figure out its meaning, look for clues around it. A clue might be in an explanation or definition given before or after the word.

Notice how *recipe* is used in the paragraph below. Find an explanation in the sentences around it.

Calm During the Storm

The weather was different today. The sky was a dark mass of clouds and the wind was still. In the distance, Sami could see bright flashes of lightning. Sami's sister Liz was afraid of storms, so Sami got out a recipe for cookies. As they followed the directions and measured the sugar and flour, they could hear loud booms of thunder. But Liz was having fun—she wasn't scared anymore.

Talk About It

Tell about weather that scares you. Use some vocabulary words.

62

Thunder Cake

written and illustrated by Patricia Polacco

Grandma looked at the horizon, drew a deep breath and said, "This is Thunder Cake baking weather, all right. Looks like a storm coming to me."

"Child, you come out from under that bed. It's
only thunder you're hearing," my grandma said.

The air was hot, heavy, and damp. A loud clap of thunder shook the house, rattled the windows, and made me grab her close.

"Steady, child," she cooed. "Unless you let go of me, we won't be able to make a Thunder Cake today!"

"Thunder Cake?" I stammered as I hugged her even closer.

"Don't pay attention to that old thunder, except to see how close the storm is getting. When you see the lightning, start counting . . . real slow. When you hear the thunder, stop counting. That number is how many miles away the storm is. Understand?" she asked. "We need to know how far away the storm is, so we have time to make the cake and get it into the oven before the storm comes, or it won't be real Thunder Cake."

Her eyes surveyed the black clouds a way off in the distance. Then she strode into the kitchen. Her worn hands pulled a thick book from the shelf above the woodstove.

"Let's find that recipe, child," she crowed as she lovingly fingered the grease-stained pages to a creased spot.

"Here it is . . . Thunder Cake!"

She carefully penned the ingredients on a piece of notepaper. "Now let's gather all the things we'll need!" she exclaimed as she scurried toward the back door.

We were by the barn door when a huge bolt
of lightning flashed. I started counting, like
Grandma told me to, "1-2-3-4-5-6-7-8-9-10."

Then the thunder ROARED!

"Ten miles . . . it's ten miles away," Grandma
said as she looked at the sky. "About an hour away,
I'd say. You'll have to hurry, child. Gather them
eggs careful-like," she said.

Eggs from mean old Nellie Peck Hen. I was
scared. I knew she would try to peck me.

"I'm here, she won't hurt you. Just get
them eggs," Grandma said softly.

The lightning flashed again. "1-2-3-4-5-6-7-8-9," I counted.

"Nine miles," Grandma reminded me.

Milk was next. Milk from old Kick Cow. As Grandma milked her, Kick Cow turned and looked mean, right at me. I was scared. She looked so big.

ZIP, went the lightning. "1-2-3-4-5-6-7-8," I counted.

BAROOOOOOOOM, went the thunder.

"Eight miles, child," Grandma croaked. "Now we have to get chocolate and sugar, and flour from the dry shed."

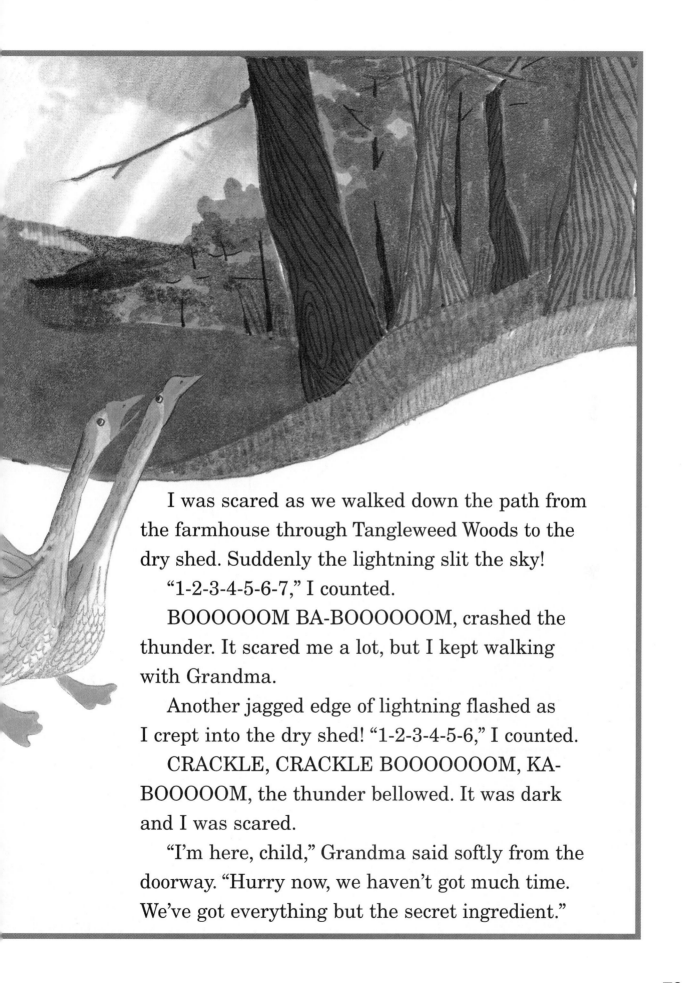

I was scared as we walked down the path from the farmhouse through Tangleweed Woods to the dry shed. Suddenly the lightning slit the sky!

"1-2-3-4-5-6-7," I counted.

BOOOOOOM BA-BOOOOOOM, crashed the thunder. It scared me a lot, but I kept walking with Grandma.

Another jagged edge of lightning flashed as I crept into the dry shed! "1-2-3-4-5-6," I counted.

CRACKLE, CRACKLE BOOOOOOOM, KA-BOOOOOM, the thunder bellowed. It was dark and I was scared.

"I'm here, child," Grandma said softly from the doorway. "Hurry now, we haven't got much time. We've got everything but the secret ingredient."

"Three overripe tomatoes and some strawberries," Grandma whispered as she squinted at the list.

I climbed up high on the trellis. The ground looked a long way down. I was scared.

"I'm here, child," she said. Her voice was steady and soft. "You won't fall."

I reached three luscious tomatoes while she picked strawberries. Lightning again!

"1-2-3-4-5," I counted.

KA-BANG BOOOOOOOOOAROOOOM, the thunder growled.

We hurried back to the house and the warm kitchen, and we measured the ingredients. I poured them into the mixing bowl while Grandma mixed. I churned butter for the frosting and melted chocolate. Finally, we poured the batter into the cake pans and put them into the oven together.

Lightning lit the kitchen! I only counted to three and the thunder RRRRUMBLED and CRASHED.

"Three miles away," Grandma said, "and the cake is in the oven. We made it! We'll have a real Thunder Cake!"

As we waited for the cake, Grandma looked out the window for a long time. "Why, you aren't afraid of thunder. You're too brave!" she said as she looked right at me.

"I'm not brave, Grandma," I said. "I was under the bed! Remember?"

"But you got out from under it," she answered, "and you got eggs from mean old Nellie Peck Hen, you got milk from old Kick Cow, you went through Tangleweed Woods to the dry shed, you climbed the trellis in the barnyard. From where I sit, only a very brave person could have done all them things!"

I thought and thought as the storm rumbled closer. She was right. I was brave!

"Brave people can't be afraid of a sound, child," she said as we spread out the tablecloth and set the table. When we were done, we hurried into the kitchen to take the cake out of the oven. After the cake had cooled, we frosted it.

Just then the lightning flashed, and this time it lit the whole sky.

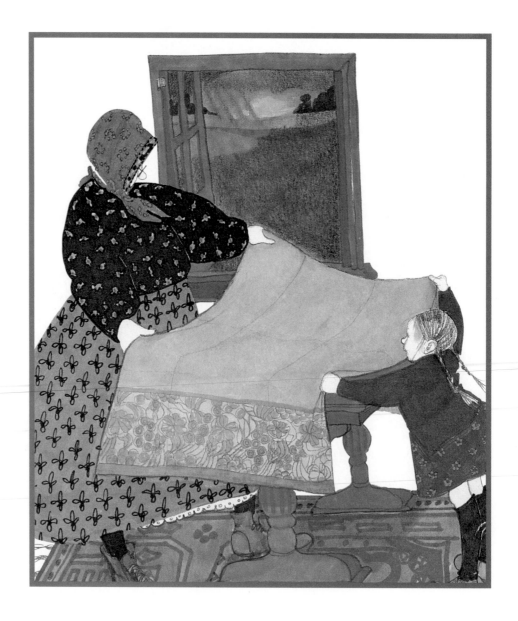

Even before the last flash had faded, the
thunder ROLLED, BOOOOOMED, CRASHED, and
BBBBAAAAARRRRROOOOOOOOMMMMMMM-
MMMED just above us. The storm was here!

"Perfect," Grandma cooed, "just perfect." She
beamed as she added the last strawberry to
the glistening chocolate frosting on top of our
Thunder Cake.

As rain poured down on our roof, Grandma cut a wedge for each of us. She poured us steaming cups of tea from the samovar.

When the thunder ROARED above us so hard it shook the windows and rattled the dishes in the cupboards, we just smiled and ate our Thunder Cake.

From that time on, I never feared the voice of thunder again.

Patricia Polacco

Patricia Polacco comes from a long line of storytellers. "My fondest memories are of sitting around a stove or open fire," she remembers, "eating apples and popping popcorn while listening to the old ones tell glorious stories about the past." Many of her relatives came from Russia. As a child, Ms. Polacco learned of Russian traditions and folk tales through these stories.

Along with *Thunder Cake,* Ms. Polacco has written and illustrated other stories about her family. *The Trees of the Dancing Goats* also takes place on her Babushka's (Grandma's) farm in Michigan. Ms. Polacco's story *Uncle Vova's Tree* is a holiday tale about traditions that her relatives brought to America from Russia.

Ms. Polacco is an expert on Russian paintings and has studied art in both the United States and Australia. She now lives in Oakland, California.

Reader Response

Open for Discussion

If you were with someone who was afraid of a storm, what would you do to help that person get over the fear?

Comprehension Check

1. Why did Grandma make a Thunder Cake?

2. Does the girl visiting her grandmother live on a farm herself? How can you tell?

3. Thunder can be frightening because it is so loud. Look through the story. What are some of the many ways that the author describes the sound thunder makes?

4. What is the **cause** and what is the **effect** in this sentence? *The girl was afraid of Nellie Peck Hen because she thought the hen would peck her.*

5. What is the **cause** and what are the **effects** in this sentence from the story? *A loud clap of thunder shook the house, rattled the windows, and made me grab her close.*

Tastiest Treats

Do you think a Thunder Cake is something you'd like to eat? What is your favorite homemade treat? Jot down notes telling how it tastes, what it looks like, and how your special treat is made. Use your notes to tell classmates about your tastiest treat.

Skill Lesson

Compare and Contrast

- We **compare** when we say how things are alike.

- We **contrast** when we say how things are different.

- Clue words, such as *yet* and *however,* can signal a comparison or a contrast.

Read "Afraid of the Dark" from *Darkness and the Butterfly* **by Ann Grifalconi.**

Write About It

Fold a sheet of paper in half the long way. Write *day* at the top left of the paper and *night* at the top right of the paper. Under the correct word, write words or phrases from the selection that compare how Osa acts during the day and at night. Compare and contrast your findings with classmates.

Afraid
of the Dark
by Ann Grifalconi

There was a bright and pretty girl named Osa who was *so* afraid of the dark, no matter what her mother or grandfather said when evening came Osa would not leave the house. She would sit in the corner hugging her knees to her chin and her eyes would grow big and black with fear.

And she would stay that way refusing food and comfort 'til she fell asleep. Then her mother would lift her gently and tuck her into bed wishing she would find some way to show Osa not to fear—but to

84

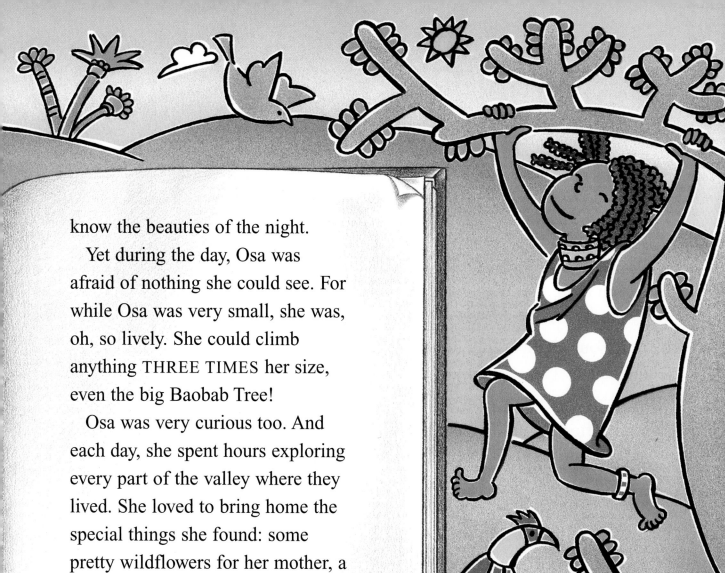

know the beauties of the night.

Yet during the day, Osa was afraid of nothing she could see. For while Osa was very small, she was, oh, so lively. She could climb anything THREE TIMES her size, even the big Baobab Tree!

Osa was very curious too. And each day, she spent hours exploring every part of the valley where they lived. She loved to bring home the special things she found: some pretty wildflowers for her mother, a bright leaf or bird's feather for her grandfather. Or just some colored stones to keep.

But when nighttime fell, fearless daytime Osa became just as fearful as before.

LOOK AHEAD TO

One Grain of Rice

In the next story, Rani teaches the raja about sharing. Read and compare and contrast Rani and the raja.

Vocabulary

Words to Know

double	reward	single
grain	palace	thief

When you read, you may come across a word you don't know. To figure out its meaning, look for clues near it. A clue might be found in an explanation given before or after the unknown word.

Read the paragraph below. Notice clues that explain what a *thief* is and does.

The Kind King

A <u>thief</u> stole jewels from the king's <u>palace</u>. The king said he would <u>reward</u> the person who caught the thief. A man said to the king, "I am the robber. I stole because my family doesn't have a <u>single</u> <u>grain</u> of oats or rice to eat." The king said, "If this is true, I will give you a job." The man thanked him and worked to pay back <u>double</u> what he stole.

Write About It

Imagine you are the thief. Write a brief thank-you note to the king. Use vocabulary words.

One Grain of Rice

BY Demi

A MATHEMATICAL FOLKTALE

Long ago in India, there lived a raja who believed that he was wise and fair, as a raja should be.

The people in his province were rice farmers. The raja decreed that everyone must give nearly all of their rice to him.

"I will store the rice safely," the raja promised the people, "so that in time of famine, everyone will have rice to eat, and no one will go hungry."

Each year, the raja's rice collectors gathered nearly all of the people's rice and carried it away to the royal storehouses.

For many years, the rice grew well. The people gave nearly all of their rice to the raja, and the storehouses were always full. But the people were left with only just enough rice to get by.

Then one year the rice grew badly, and there was famine and hunger. The people had no rice to give to the raja, and they had no rice to eat.

The raja's ministers implored him, "Your Highness, let us open the royal storehouses and give the rice to the people, as you promised."

"No!" cried the raja. "How do I know how long the famine may last? I must have the rice for myself. Promise or no promise, a raja must not go hungry!"

Time went on, and the people grew more and more hungry. But the raja would not give out the rice.

One day, the raja ordered a feast for himself and his court— as, it seemed to him, a raja should now and then, even when there is famine.

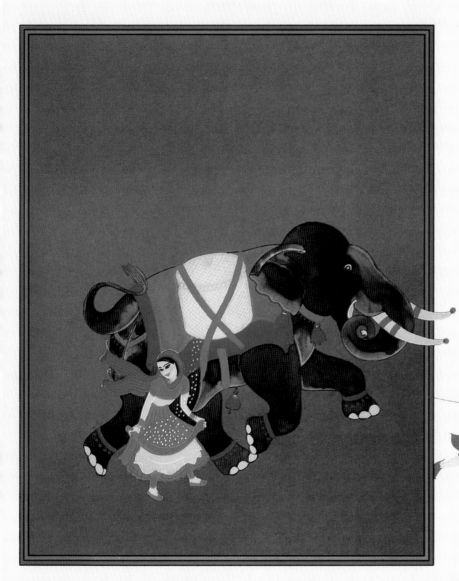

A servant led an elephant from a royal storehouse to the palace, carrying two full baskets of rice.

A village girl named Rani saw that a trickle of rice was falling from one of the baskets. Quickly she jumped up and walked along beside the elephant, catching the falling rice in her skirt. She was clever, and she began to make a plan.

At the palace, a guard cried, "Halt, thief! Where are you going with that rice?"

"I am not a thief," Rani replied. "This rice fell from one of the baskets, and I am returning it now to the raja."

When the raja heard about Rani's good deed, he asked his ministers to bring her before him.

"I wish to reward you for returning what belongs to me," the raja said to Rani. "Ask me for anything, and you shall have it."

"Your Highness," said Rani, "I do not deserve any reward at all. But if you wish, you may give me one grain of rice."

"Only one grain of rice?" exclaimed the raja. "Surely you will allow me to reward you more plentifully, as a raja should."

"Very well," said Rani. "If it pleases Your Highness, you may reward me in this way. Today, you will give me a single grain of rice. Then, each day for thirty days you will give me double the rice you gave me the day before. Thus, tomorrow you will give me two grains of rice, the next day four grains of rice, and so on for thirty days."

"This seems still to be a modest reward," said the raja. "But you shall have it."

And Rani was presented with a single grain of rice.

The next day, Rani was presented with two grains of rice.

And the following day, Rani was presented with four grains of rice.

On the ninth day, Rani was presented with two hundred and fifty-six grains of rice. She had received in all five hundred and eleven grains of rice, only enough for a small handful.

"This girl is honest, but not very clever," thought the raja. "She would have gained more rice by keeping what fell into her skirt!"

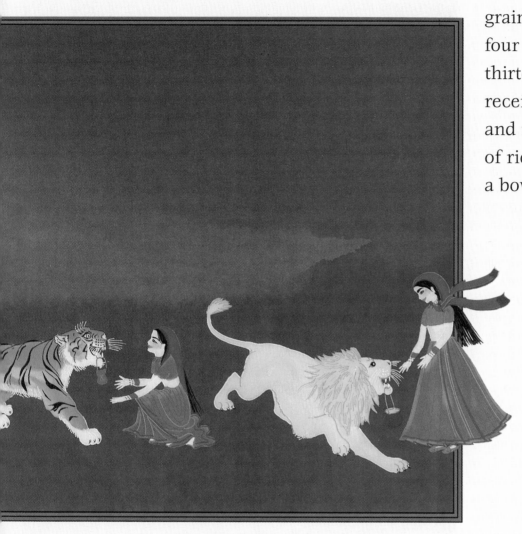

On the twelfth day, Rani received two thousand and forty-eight grains of rice, about four handfuls. On the thirteenth day, she received four thousand and ninety-six grains of rice, enough to fill a bowl.

On the sixteenth day, Rani was presented with a bag containing thirty-two thousand, seven hundred and sixty-eight grains of rice. All together she had enough rice for two full bags.

"This doubling adds up to more rice than I expected!" thought the raja. "But surely her reward won't amount to much more."

On the twentieth day, Rani was presented with sixteen more bags filled with rice.

On the twenty-first day, she received one million, forty-eight thousand, five hundred and seventy-six grains of rice, enough to fill a basket.

On the twenty-fourth day, Rani was presented with eight million, three hundred and eighty-eight thousand, six hundred and eight grains of rice—enough to fill eight baskets, which were carried to her by eight royal deer.

On the twenty-seventh day, thirty-two Brahma bulls were needed to deliver sixty-four baskets of rice.

The raja was deeply troubled. "One grain of rice has grown very great indeed," he thought. "But I shall fulfill the reward to the end, as a raja should."

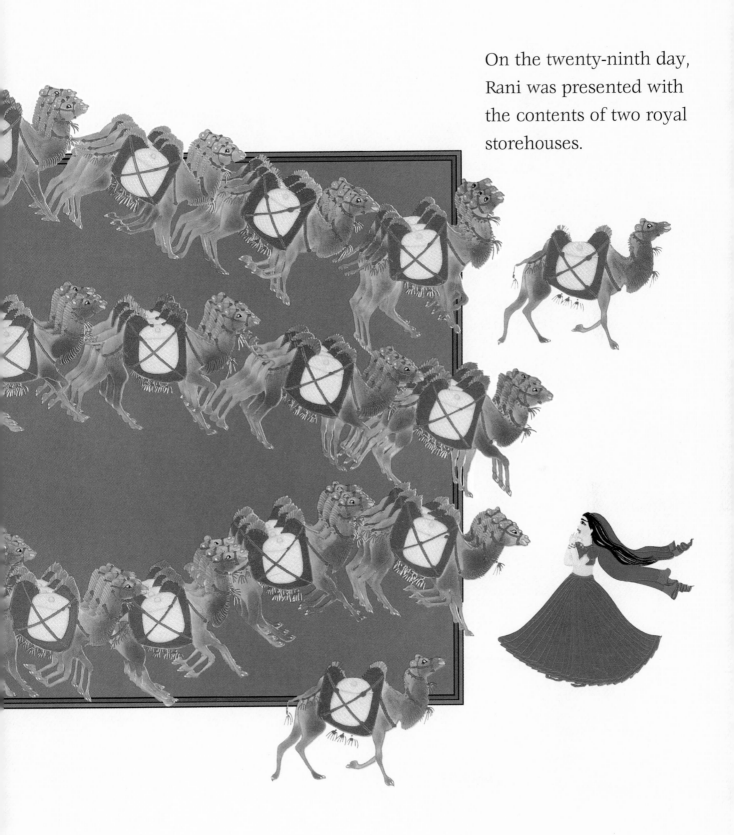

On the twenty-ninth day, Rani was presented with the contents of two royal storehouses.

On the thirtieth and final day, two hundred and fifty-six elephants crossed the province, carrying the contents of the last four royal storehouses—five hundred and thirty-six million, eight hundred and seventy thousand, nine hundred and twelve grains of rice.

All together, Rani had received more than one billion grains of rice. The raja had no more rice to give. "And what will you do with this rice," said the raja with a sigh, "now that I have none?"

"I shall give it to all the hungry people," said Rani. "And I shall leave a basket of rice for you, too, if you promise from now on to take only as much rice as you need."

"I promise," said the raja.

And for the rest of his days, the raja was truly wise and fair, as a raja should be.

About the Author/Illustrator

Demi

Demi Hitz prefers to be known by her first name only. Demi has been around artists all of her life. Her mother was an artist and her father was an architect and actor. When she was younger, Demi lived in India for two years. Her love of Indian art shows up in *The Hallowed Horse: A Folktale from India* and *One Grain of Rice.*

Demi loves to travel. Her travels have influenced her to write books about different people and places around the world. She has written about the explorer Marco Polo and his travels through Asia. She also has written books about China: *Dragon Kites and Dragonflies,* *A Chinese Zoo,* and *Chen Ping and His Magic Axe.*

Several of Demi's books have won awards, including *The Empty Pot* and *The Nightingale.*

In addition to writing and illustrating books, Demi gives speeches at colleges and libraries about her work.

Reader Response

Open for Discussion

When would Rani be a good person to have with you? Explain.

Comprehension Check

1. Both *Ananse's Feast* and *One Grain of Rice* take place during a famine in which some characters feast while others go hungry. Make a list for the two stories that show which characters feast and which characters go hungry.

2. Would the raja have given Rani as much rice if she had asked for it all at once? What in the story supports your answer?

3. What kind of person is Rani? Use examples from the story to support your ideas.

4. **Compare and contrast** the lives of the raja and the rice farmers. Where do they live? Who is in charge?

5. **Contrast** the raja's plan for the rice at the beginning of the story with what the raja really did with the rice.

An Indian Zoo

Draw one of the animals from the story on a large index card. Then cut out the animal shape. Write a fact about that animal on the cutout. With classmates collect your fact cards on a bulletin board to make an Indian Zoo. Discuss which animals live in India that are not found where you live.

Where does RICE come from?

by Lynne Merrison

Rice comes from rice plants that are usually grown in flooded fields called **paddies**. In paddies, the roots of the rice plants are kept under water. The head of a rice plant is called a **panicle**. It grows on a stalk above long, flat leaves. The panicle has small flowers called **spikelets** that produce the grains of raw rice.

Reading an Informational Article

✓ **Read the title.** It usually tells what the text is all about.

✓ **Look for pictures or other graphic sources.** Pictures and graphs help explain parts of the article or give more information.

✓ **Look for the main idea.** Each paragraph in the text will probably have a main idea and details. Each main idea will relate to the topic of the text.

Focus Your Reading

This informational article tells you about rice. As you read, think about how Rani or the raja could have used this information.

Rice fields, or paddies, that are laid out in terraces in the Philippines

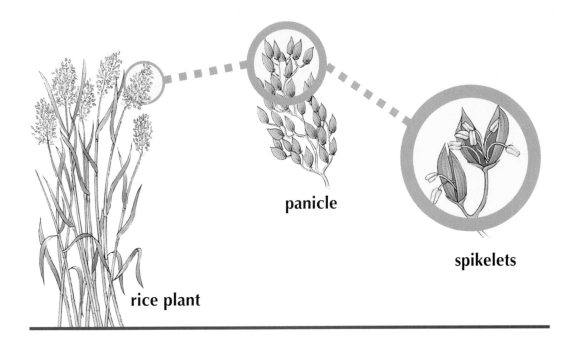

rice plant

panicle

spikelets

Rice is grown in about one hundred countries. It needs plenty of water and sunshine, so tropical and subtropical climates are ideal for growing rice. The monsoon regions of Southeast Asia are especially well suited to rice farming. China, India, and other Asian countries produce about 90 percent of the world's rice. It is also grown in parts of the United States, South America, Europe, and Africa.

LEADING RICE-GROWING STATES

Tons of Rice Produced in a Year

State	
Arkansas	❘❘❘❘❘❘❘❘❘❘❘❘❘❘❘❘
California	❘❘❘❘❘❘❘❘❘
Louisiana	❘❘❘❘❘❘❘
Texas	❘❘❘❘❘
Mississippi	❘❘❘

❘ = about 250,000 tons of rice

Figures from the U.S. Department of Agriculture are three-year averages (1994–1996).

Predicting

- To **predict** means to tell what you think might happen next in a story judging from what has already happened.

- A prediction is what you think will happen.

- As you read, use the clues in the story and what you know from real life to help you decide what might happen next.

Read "What to Do with an Old Hat," from *Uncle Nacho's Hat* by **Harriet Rohmer.**

UNCLE NACHO'S HAT

EL SOMBRERO DEL TÍO NACHO

Talk About It

1. What clues from the story and from your own life helped you make your prediction?

2. How close was your prediction to what really happened?

What to Do with an Old Hat

by Harriet Rohmer

Uncle Nacho put on the new hat and looked at himself in the mirror.

"See how handsome it makes you look, Uncle Nacho," said Ambrosia.

"It's true. All the girls will fall in love with me."

"That's for sure, Uncle Nacho. Well, I have to go to school now. I'll come by later."

"Take care of yourself, Ambrosia. And thank you for the hat."

"Now I have a new hat," said Uncle Nacho to himself. "But what am I going to do with this old hat that's not good for anything anymore?"

"Hat," he said to his old hat. "What am I going to do with you?"

"I know. I'll put you in my trunk."

"Wait a minute. What if mice get in and start to eat you? No, no, no. I'd better not put you in my trunk."

Predict what Uncle Nacho will do with his old hat.

"But hat, you're really not good for anything anymore," said Uncle Nacho. "You don't keep me dry in the rain. I should throw you away. I'll just take you outside right now and throw you away in the street."

"Wait a minute. I think I see a car coming. You might get run over. No, no, no. I'd better not throw you away in the street."

"But hat, you're really not good for anything anymore," said Uncle Nacho. "You don't keep the sun off my head. I should throw you away. I'll just take you outside right now and throw you in the trash."

"There! May some good man find you. Someone who will appreciate you. A decent person."

The Woman Who Outshone the Sun

In the next story, Lucia, a stranger, comes to town and takes the town's river. Read and see if you can predict what the townspeople will do.

Vocabulary

Words to Know

cruel   spied   arrived

shone   thirst   respect

astonished   excitement

Words with opposite meanings are **antonyms.** You can figure out the meaning of an unknown word by looking for a clue in nearby words. Sometimes this clue is an antonym.

Read the paragraph below. Notice how *left* helps you understand its antonym *arrived*.

Heroes in the Neighborhood

<u>Cruel</u> winds whipped the trees and shook houses. In the <u>excitement</u> of the storm, I was <u>astonished</u> to see my tree house fly through the air! Finally, the storm left almost as quickly as it had <u>arrived</u>. I <u>spied</u> rescue workers coming up the street. I <u>respect</u> them, because they help people. I even gave one water to ease his <u>thirst</u>. The sun soon <u>shone</u> and made the damage look even worse.

Write About It

Write a headline about a hero you know. Use some vocabulary words.

114

THE WOMAN WHO OUTSHONE THE SUN

THE LEGEND OF LUCIA ZENTENO

from a poem by Alejandro Cruz Martinez • pictures by Fernando Olivera
retold by Harriet Rohmer and David Schecter

The day Lucia Zenteno arrived, everyone in the village was astonished. No one knew where she came from. Yet they all saw that she was amazingly beautiful, and that she brought thousands of dancing butterflies and brightly-colored flowers on her skirts. She walked softly yet with quiet dignity, her long, unbraided hair flowing behind her. A loyal iguana walked at her side.

No one knew who she was, but they did know that nothing shone as brightly as Lucia Zenteno. Some people said that Lucia Zenteno outshone the sun. Others said that her glorious hair seemed to block out the light.

Everyone felt a little afraid of someone so wonderful and yet so strange.

There used to be a river that ran by the town, almost the same river that runs by there now. And people said that when Lucia Zenteno went there to bathe, the river fell in love with her. The water rose from its bed and began to flow through her shining black hair.

When Lucia finished bathing, she would sit by the river and comb out her hair with a comb made from the wood of the mesquite tree. And when she did, the water, the fishes, and the otters would flow out of her hair and return to the river once more.

The old people of the village said that although Lucia was different from them, she should be honored and treated with respect. She understood the ways of nature, they said.

But some people did not listen to the elders. They were afraid of Lucia's powers, which they did not understand. And so they refused to answer Lucia's greetings, or offer their friendship. They called her cruel names and spied on her day and night.

Lucia did not return the meanness of the people.
She kept to herself and continued to walk with her
head held high.

Her quiet dignity angered some of the people. They
whispered that Lucia must be trying to harm them.
People became more afraid of Lucia and so they treated
her more cruelly. Finally, they drove her from the village.

Lucia went down to the river one last time to say good-bye. As always, the water rose to greet her and began to flow through her glorious hair. But this time when she tried to comb the river out of her hair, the river would not leave her.

And so, when Lucia Zenteno left the village, the river and the fishes and the otters went with her, leaving only a dry, winding riverbed, a serpent of sand where the water had been.

Everyone saw that Lucia Zenteno was leaving and that the river, the fishes, and the otters were leaving with her. The people were filled with despair. They had never imagined that their beautiful river would ever leave them, no matter what they did.

Where once there had been green trees and cool breezes, now no more rain fell, no birds sang, no otters played. The people and their animals suffered from thirst. People began to understand, as never before, how much the river, the fishes, the otters, even the trees and birds had meant to the village. They began to understand how much the river had loved Lucia Zenteno.

The elders said that everyone must search for Lucia
and beg her forgiveness. Some people did not want to.
They were too afraid. But when the drought continued,
everyone finally agreed to follow the elders' advice. And
so the whole village set out in search of Lucia.

After many days of walking, the people found the iguana cave where Lucia had gone to seek refuge. Lucia was waiting for them, but they could not see her face. She had turned her back to the people.

At first no one dared say a word. Then two children called out, "Lucia, we have come to ask your forgiveness. Please have mercy on us and return our river!"

ucia Zenteno turned and looked at the people. She
saw their frightened, tired faces, and she felt compassion
for them. At last she spoke. "I will ask the river to return
to you," she said. "But just as the river gives water to all
who are thirsty, no matter who they are, so you must
learn to treat everyone with kindness, even those who
seem different from you."

The people remembered how they had treated Lucia, and they hung their heads in shame.

Seeing that the people were truly sorry for what they had done, Lucia returned with them to the village and began to comb out her hair. She combed out the water, she combed out the fishes, she combed out the otters, and she kept on combing until the river had returned once more to where it belonged.

The people were overjoyed to have their river again. They poured water over themselves and over their animals, they jumped into the river, and they laughed and cried with happiness.

In all the excitement, no one noticed at first that Lucia had disappeared again. When the children asked the elders where she had gone, the elders replied that Lucia had not really left them. Though they would not be able to see her, she would always be there, guiding and protecting them, helping them to live with love and understanding in their hearts.

About the Authors

ALEJANDRO CRUZ MARTINEZ, HARRIET ROHMER, DAVID SCHECTER

Alejandro Cruz Martinez was a Zapotec Indian poet who lived in Oaxaca, Mexico. Because he wanted the history of his people to live on, Mr. Martinez collected stories and wrote them down as poems. One of these poems is about the legendary character Lucia Zenteno. After Mr. Martinez died, his widow sent the poem to a children's book publisher. The publisher showed the poem to Harriet Rohmer and David Schecter, who turned it into a story.

About the Illustrator

FERNANDO OLIVERA

Fernando Olivera is an artist who was a good friend of Alejandro Cruz Martinez. When Mr. Martinez told him the story, Mr. Olivera was so interested that he painted pictures of what he thought Lucia Zenteno looked like. After Mr. Martinez died and the book about Lucia was written, Mr. Olivera created the pictures to go with it. Mr. Olivera lives in the state of Oaxaca, Mexico.

Reader Response

Open for Discussion

Would you like to live in the village after Lucia Zenteno took the river away with her? Why or why not?

Comprehension Check

1. In folk tales or fables the characters often either teach a lesson or learn a lesson. With that in mind, why do you think Lucia came to the village?

2. Why was the river important to the people of the village?

3. How will the villagers treat the next stranger who comes to their village? Why do you think so?

4. What did you **predict** would happen when Lucia left the village the first time? Were you right?

5. Did you **predict** what Lucia would do when the villagers went to the iguana cave to see her? What did you base your prediction on?

Welcoming Committee

Think about welcoming newcomers to your class. What would you tell them? What would you do? In a small group, take turns being the newcomer and the other members of the class, acting out a brief scene of welcome.

131

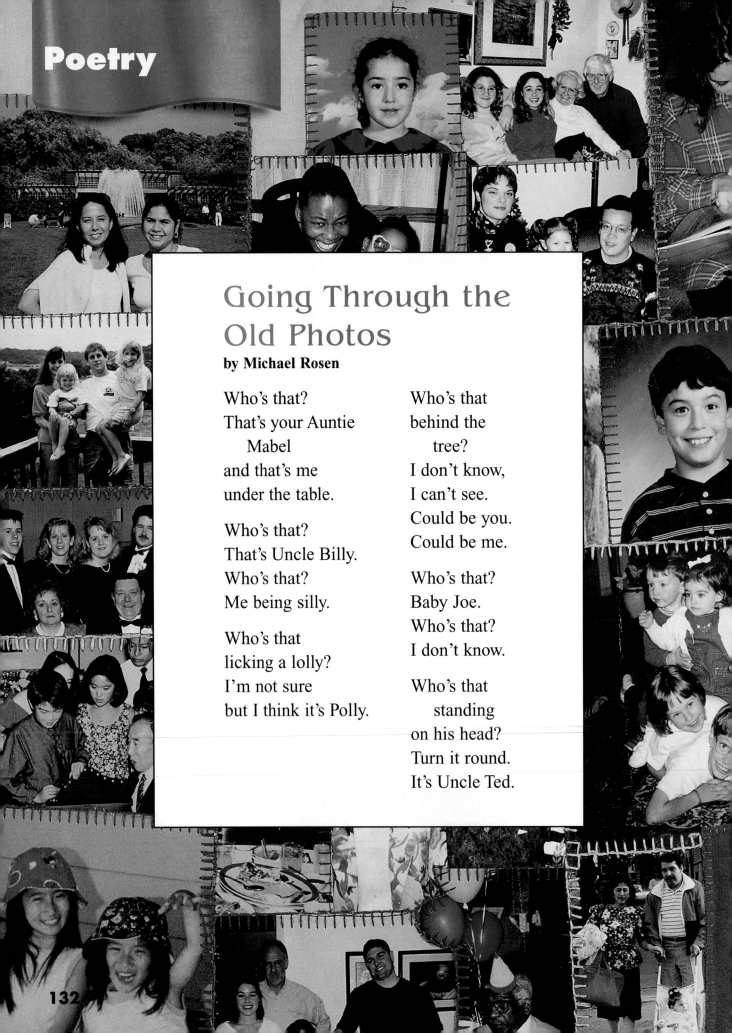

Going Through the Old Photos

by Michael Rosen

Who's that?
That's your Auntie
    Mabel
and that's me
under the table.

Who's that?
That's Uncle Billy.
Who's that?
Me being silly.

Who's that
licking a lolly?
I'm not sure
but I think it's Polly.

Who's that
behind the
    tree?
I don't know,
I can't see.
Could be you.
Could be me.

Who's that?
Baby Joe.
Who's that?
I don't know.

Who's that
    standing
on his head?
Turn it round.
It's Uncle Ted.

Quilt

by Janet S. Wong

Our family
is a quilt

of odd remnants
patched together

in a strange
pattern,

threads fraying,
fabric wearing thin—

but made to keep
its warmth

even in bitter
cold.

The Stars

by Nelly Palacio Jaramillo

Always quiet,
Always blinking,
By day sleeping,
At night winking.

Las estrellas

por Nelly Palacio Jaramillo

Siempre quietas,
Siempre inquietas,
Durmiendo de día,
De noche despiertas.

Sky Bear

by the Mohawk Indians

Long ago,
three hunters and their little dog
found the tracks of a giant bear.
They followed those tracks
all through the day
and even though it was almost dark
they did not stop, but continued on.
They saw that bear now, climbing
    up
a hill, which glittered
with new-fallen snow.
They ran hard to catch it,
but the bear was too fast.
They ran and they ran, climbing
up and up until one of the hunters
    said,
"Brothers, look down."
They did and saw they
were high above Earth.
That bear was Sky Bear,
running on through the stars.
Look up now
and you will see her,
circling the sky.

Are We There Yet?

How can visits to other times and other places make our lives better?

Making Judgments

- A judgment is your opinion about a character, a situation, an action, or an idea in a story or article.

- When you **make judgments,** you use what you already know and what you have read.

- Find sentences from the story or article to support your judgments.

Read "Grandpa's Memories" from *Grandpa Is a Flyer* by Sanna Anderson Baker.

Talk About It

1. Is the boy being fair when he says he will weed the garden if his dad takes him to see the plane? Why or why not?

2. Does Dad do the right thing in taking the boy to see the plane? Explain.

Grandpa's Memories
by Sanna Anderson Baker

Once I'd seen a plane in the sky I couldn't think about anything else. Every day my brother, Erik, and I rushed through our chores. We had to milk our cow, gather eggs, haul water, and bring in wood so we could get inside to hear "The Air Adventures of Jimmy Allen."

One day the noise of a plane nearly raised our roof. I banged out the screen door and squinted to see. It was so low and so loud, I knew the plane had to be landing. I begged Dad to take me.

Finally, when I promised to weed the garden, he said, "Get in!" We rattled up one dusty road and

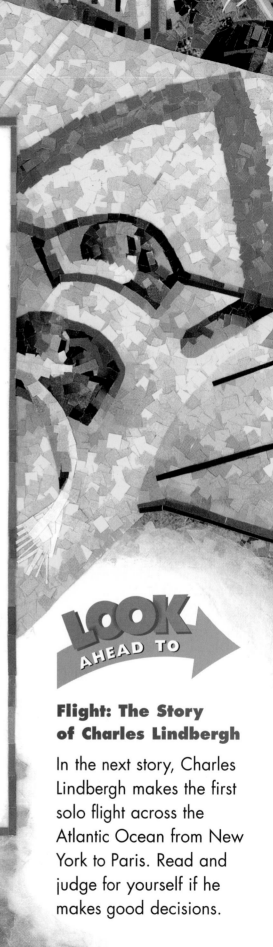

down another in the Model A until we saw the plane sitting in Conrad Johnson's field.

The pilot was dressed like Lindbergh in a flying suit and boots, but he had his goggles off, so I could see it wasn't Lindy. He was a barnstormer, a pilot who'd land in a farmer's field and sell rides.

"Ready for a ride, young man?" he asked me. I just shook my head. I didn't have any money, and I knew my dad didn't, either. But it didn't cost anything to look, and I looked over every inch of that Jenny.

After awhile our neighbor R.V. Carlson handed over his money and climbed into the cockpit. Seeing that plane take off was like watching a miracle.

That night I told Erik, "By next summer I'm going to fly."

LOOK AHEAD TO

Flight: The Story of Charles Lindbergh

In the next story, Charles Lindbergh makes the first solo flight across the Atlantic Ocean from New York to Paris. Read and judge for yourself if he makes good decisions.

Vocabulary

Words to Know

compasses   engine   flight
instruments   route   soars

Words that are pronounced the same but have different spellings and meanings are called **homophones.** To understand the meaning of a homophone look for clues around the word.

Read the paragraph below. Why is the word *soars* used below and not *sores?*

Flight Journal

I check my flight instruments. My compasses show I head straight east, so I am on the correct route. If my engine doesn't run into trouble, I should be in Paris in eight hours. As my plane soars through the sky, I think about the landing ahead. What a flight this is—my first time across the Atlantic Ocean alone!

Write About It

Imagine you're landing the plane. Write a journal entry using vocabulary words.

FLIGHT

The Journey of Charles Lindbergh

by Robert Burleigh • illustrated by Mike Wimmer

It is 1927, and his name is Charles Lindbergh.
Later they will call him the Lone Eagle. Later they
will call him Lucky Lindy. But not now. Now it is
May 20, 1927, and he is standing in the still-dark
dawn. He watches rain drizzle down on the airfield.
And on his small airplane. The airplane has a
name painted on its side: *Spirit of St. Louis*.

Lindbergh is nearly as tall as the plane itself. And yet—he is about to attempt what no one has done before: to fly—without a stop—from New York to Paris, France. Over 3,600 miles away. Across the Atlantic Ocean. Alone.

He climbs into the boxlike cockpit that will be his only home for many, many hours. He clicks on the engine. He listens as it catches, gurgles, and roars. A few friends are here to say good-bye. They are only a few feet away, and yet to Lindbergh how far off they seem. They look up at him and wave. "Good luck! Keep safe!"

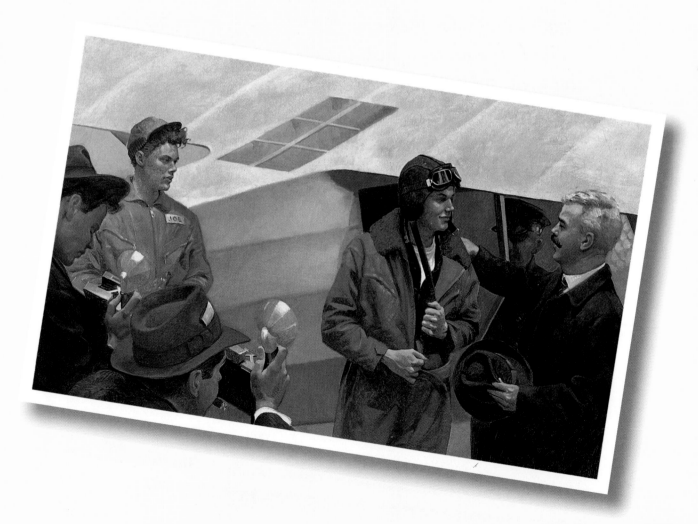

A telephone wire stretches across the far end of the field. To touch this wire will plunge the plane to the ground. There is an extra fuel tank in front of the cockpit. Because of this, Lindbergh cannot see straight ahead. Will the *Spirit of St. Louis*, with its over 5,000 pounds, rise into the air? To keep the plane lighter, Lindbergh is leaving behind his radio and parachute. Will that be enough?

He has been up all night getting ready. A thought runs back and forth through his mind: It is still possible to turn back. To return home. And yet another thought is stronger: I have been waiting my entire life for this flight. Lindbergh lowers his goggles and nods his head: "Go!"

Men on each side push to help the plane roll over the soggy ground. The little plane bumps forward, gaining speed. The wheels leave the ground, then touch back. The plane seems to hop, taking its "last bow to earth." On the third try it stays aloft. It soars above the wire by only twenty feet. The

Spirit of St. Louis rises in the air. It is 7:52 in the morning, New York time. Lindbergh points his plane toward the Atlantic and beyond, toward Paris. Over thirty hours away.

He gazes down in the morning light. How far off Paris seems—across the long ocean. He plans to follow the coastline, flying northeast. The land's edge looks to him like green fingers, pointing at the dark sea. To see ahead, Lindbergh pokes a small homemade periscope out the side of the cockpit. Sometimes he flies very close to the water. Just ten feet above the waves. He knows that at this low height the plane glides more smoothly. The plane drones on. It cruises at about 100 miles an hour. At this rate, he will have enough fuel to reach his destination, but only if he stays on course.

Beside him in the cockpit is a little book. He keeps a diary as he goes all day long, hour by hour. It is as if he were speaking to himself. He wants to remember everything. Because no one else will ever really know. At 12:08 he flies above Nova Scotia. Just after 4:00 he flies above the coast of Newfoundland. At dusk he looks down and sees icebergs! In his diary he calls them "White pyramids . . . White patches on a blackened sea; sentries of the Arctic." He wonders what lies ahead.

The sun sets far behind the plane. Lindbergh flies over St. John's, Newfoundland, the last point of land in North America. Now he can no longer follow the land's edge for direction. He must chart his course carefully. The slightest movement could send him miles off course and risk the fuel supply. He follows two compasses and the stars to navigate. As long as the sky is clear, he is safe. But he must stay awake. He writes: "Now I must cross not one, but two oceans: One of night and one of water."

Time passes slowly. It is almost 9:00 at night, Lindbergh's thirteenth hour in the air. He has completed one-third of the flight. He moves through dense, curling fog, lit ghostly white by the moon. He suddenly enters a huge stormcloud. The plane shimmers, moving up and down in the uniform blackness. He wonders: Can I fly above it? Slowly, he soars to 10,500 feet. Here it is clear—but very, very cold. He extends his arm outside the cockpit and feels "stinging pinpricks."

He clicks on his small flashlight and peers out: Heavy ice has formed on the plane's wings. He cannot risk his instruments' icing up. He points the *Spirit of St. Louis* back down. The wings quiver as they slice through the turbulent air. The fog continues but now, at least, the air is warmer. The ice begins to melt and Lindbergh roars ahead, through the fog and clouds, to Paris over 2,000 miles away.

Space and time and deep, deep darkness: It is the other side of midnight, the loneliest hours. Lindbergh has been awake for almost fifty hours straight. He is closer to Europe than America. Now there is no turning back, only moving forward. He dozes for a minute and then jerks awake. One of the plane's wings is dipping crazily.

In a sudden rush of fear, he grabs for the throttle. He gropes for the steady center with his heart pounding. As he feels the leveling wings, he lets out breath. He repeats over and over to himself: *I must not sleep, I must not sleep*. Here, high above the churning ocean, to sleep is to die!

These are some of the things he does to stay awake: He leans his face near the open window to feel the cold air. He holds his eyelids up with his fingers to keep them from closing. He remembers growing up on a farm in Minnesota. He remembers being a trick pilot, and walking out on a plane's wings. He remembers the people in St. Louis who

paid for this plane. Sometimes he takes a sip of
water from his canteen. He also has five chicken
sandwiches with him. That is all the food he has
brought. But he eats nothing. It is easier to stay
awake on an empty stomach. His body cries for
sleep. He loses track of time. The night is endless.
He wishes for the sun to rise.

Dawn comes slowly, growing out of the gray mist. "Will the fog never end?" he wonders. The clouds change color: "from green to gray, and from gray to red and gold." Lindbergh has been in the air for twenty-three hours. He is 2,300 miles from New York and has 1,300 miles to go. He feels completely alone in the world. He feels as if he were "flying through all eternity." He tries to stay on course. But because of his constantly curving route, he is not always sure. Here and there, the clouds seem to break apart. He sees, far below him, the ocean. From high up it is like a great blue shaft, with gray walls. Then he flies into the clouds again. Into the unchanging mist.

The day comes on, brighter and warmer. Sometimes he imagines he sees land. No: it is only the flickering shapes of the clouds. And water, water, water, endless water. It is 7:30 in the morning in New York, and Paris is over a thousand miles away. "There's no alternative but death and failure," he writes. Flying closer to the water, Lindbergh sights a porpoise, leaping above the waves. He spies a seagull. Then fishing boats. Something quickens in Lindbergh's blood. He guides the *Spirit of St. Louis* carefully down and down, to just above a boat. He throttles the plane and calls out a question: "Which way," he shouts, "is Ireland?" He hopes for a word. He longs for a wave, ". . . a warmer welcome back to the fellowship of men." It is 10:52 in the morning, New York time.

Lindbergh sees, in the distance, low mountains. Now he is awake with new hope. Land is near. He quickly unfolds a map across his knees. He flies over the southern tip of Ireland. He is right on course! Cows graze on green hills. People in horse-drawn carts look up and wave. He could land in Ireland but decides to go on. He wants to complete his dream.

It is 1:52 in the afternoon, New York time, as he crosses England. It is Lindbergh's thirty-first hour in the air. He crosses more water. The wide day is slowly ebbing toward twilight. When he sees land—the coast of France—children run out of their houses and watch him fly by. He continues on.

Then Lindbergh spies a glow ahead of him. Paris! *I am here, I am here.* A great joy wells up inside him. For a moment, he does not want the flight ever to end. Huddled inside his tiny box-house, folded in the dense hum of the airplane's engine, he loves this strange closeness to the clouds and sky. It is 4:52 in the afternoon, New York time. Lindbergh's thirty-fourth hour in the air.

From above, all Lindbergh sees are many, many small lights. But now he must concentrate on just one thing: "the sod coming up to meet me."

Closer, closer, closer: The plane touches the ground. It bounces, rolls, hugs the solid earth. It is 10:22, Paris time. The flight has taken thirty-three and a half hours.

Thousands of people are running toward the plane. For a moment, Lindbergh is dazed. It seems to him as if he were "drowning in a great sea." People surround the plane, cheering. But Lindbergh can hardly hear them. His ears seem to have been deafened by the hours of roaring engine.

Crowds pull him out of the cockpit. Men and women are calling his name, over and over.

They carry him on their shoulders. Others begin to tear pieces of the plane. More than anything else, Lindbergh wants to save the *Spirit of St. Louis*. His first words are a question: "Are there any mechanics here?" But no one speaks English. Finally, two French aviators arrive to help him. Policemen guard the plane. The aviators take Lindbergh away from the still-cheering crowd.

In the airfield's hangar, he tells the story of his flight to the other pilots: The cramped cockpit, the aloneness, the long, long night. Meanwhile, unknown to Lindbergh, newspaper headlines all over the world are beginning to blazon the news: AMERICAN HERO SAFE IN PARIS! Lindbergh is driven off to the American Embassy. He answers more questions about his flight. He has not slept in over sixty hours. Finally, at 4:15 in the morning he goes to bed.

When he wakes, his life will be changed forever. When he wakes, there will be huge parades and medals and speeches. He will be the most famous man in the world.

It is the year 1927. It is 1927, and his name is Charles Lindbergh.

About the Author
Robert Burleigh

As a child, Robert Burleigh mostly liked sports. "I do remember writing a little rhymed poem (about a cowboy) as a very young child, which I still have," he recalls. When he grew up, Mr. Burleigh got a job at a publishing company. A big part of his job there was writing scripts for videos and filmstrips. This helped him to become a better writer.

About the Illustrator
Mike Wimmer

As an artist, Mike Wimmer started young. "Comic book heroes and sports figures were my main subjects." He also read classic adventure stories like *Robinson Crusoe.* "I didn't know what an illustrator was," Mr. Wimmer remembers, "but I did know that someone painted these pictures and that I wanted to be that person." Now he has become a well-respected illustrator himself.

Reader Response

Open for Discussion

Pretend you are an invisible passenger with Lindbergh. What did you see, hear, feel?

Comprehension Check

1. Today's airplanes have very high-tech equipment for navigation, but Lindbergh had very little help finding his way. List the things Lindbergh used to navigate from New York to Paris.

2. Was Lindbergh afraid during his flight? Point out parts of the text that support your answer.

3. Why would the people of St. Louis have been especially interested in Lindbergh's flight?

4. Lindbergh used many tricks for staying awake. **Make a judgment** about whether they were good tricks. Support your response with facts from the story.

5. Everyone was excited about Lindbergh's flight. **Make a judgment** about why people today aren't as interested when someone flies across the Atlantic. Support your answer with facts.

Press Conference

In a small group, write out questions that reporters might have asked Lindbergh at the first press conference after his flight. Take turns being Lindbergh and reporters to act out a press conference.

A Place in the Sky

by Ron Fridell

Have you ever dreamed that you could fly a plane? Bessie Coleman had that dream, and she made that dream come true, but it wasn't easy.

Bessie Coleman was born in Atlanta, Texas, in 1893. During World War I (1914–1918), she read all about the daring pilots who fought each other in the sky over Europe. *I belong up there too,* she decided.

But no flying school in America would take Bessie Coleman. In the early 1900s, flying was still new — and dangerous. Planes had open cockpits, and crashes were so common that pilots were known as "flying fools." Women pilots were rare, and an African American woman pilot? Never. There was no place in the sky for Bessie Coleman, not in America.

During her first air shows, Bessie tried out different outfits. Many of them looked like military uniforms.

Reading Across Texts

Reading a Biography

✓ **Read the title.** It may give you clues about the person you are reading about.

✓ **Read the paragraphs carefully.** The author may choose to write about only part of a person's life. Important details are given, but not all the interesting details about the person's whole life.

Focus Your Reading

This biographical sketch (short biography) gives some information about Bessie Coleman. As you read, think about how she and Charles Lindbergh were alike.

Then Bessie read about Americans who'd gone to France to find their place in the sky. Jacques Bullard, an African American pilot, flew with the French in the war. Harriet Quimby, the first American woman flyer, went to France to get her pilot's license. If they could do it, so could Bessie Coleman.

She made the trip across the Atlantic by ocean liner, landing in France in November of 1920. Not long after that she began taking flying lessons. On June 15, 1921, Bessie Coleman earned her pilot's license. She'd found her place in the sky.

When Bessie returned to the U.S., she brought a new dream back with her. She wanted to open her own flying school and

Bessie's first airplane was a Curtiss JN-4, or Jenny. It was made mainly of wires, wood, and canvas. Even with careful maintenance the engine often stalled in flight.

teach other black women and men to fly. To make this dream come true, she flew around the country putting on air shows. During one of these shows, in Orlando, Florida, in 1926, a wrench slid into the control gears, and her plane went into a dive. Bessie was thrown from the cockpit—this was before pilots wore seatbelts—and hurled to her death.

Nearly five thousand people attended Bessie Coleman's funeral. They came to honor the first African American woman to pilot a plane. In the years to come many other African American women and men would find their own place in the sky, thanks in part to Bessie Coleman.

In 1995 the U.S. Postal Service issued a 32-cent stamp in honor of Bessie Coleman, the first African American woman pilot.

Photographs like this were likely to be printed in black-owned newspapers in areas where Bessie made her flights.

Fact and Opinion

- A **statement of fact** can be proved true or false.

- A **statement of opinion** is what someone believes or thinks and cannot be proved true or false.

- Words that express what someone feels or thinks, such as *believe, could, like,* and *good,* are clues to a statement of opinion.

Read "Moving Along on Bike Trails" by Stewart Warren from *The Herald News.*

Write About It

1. Find a statement of opinion that tells what *could* be done. Write it down.

2. Find a statement of fact that tells why a bike trail would be a good idea. Write it down.

Moving Along on Bike Trails

by Stewart Warren, Staff Writer

PLAINFIELD—As Kathy Felix and Michelle Bigger drove Monday to the meeting on the park district's bike path plan, they realized pedaling would be faster.

The two neighbors, residents of the Indian Oaks subdivision, got stuck in traffic while trying to get to the Plainfield Township Park District's administration offices, 100 W. Ottawa St.

"If there had been a clear way across Illinois 59, we could have been here in 10 minutes," Bigger said.

Like many other people in the village, Felix and Bigger want more places to ride their bicycles.

"We take our kids out biking all the time," Felix said. "Some of the back roads are so busy, we can't take them without fear."

To meet the need, park district officials want to create a township-wide bike trail system to serve everyone—people who ride for recreation, and those who use bikes as transportation.

"Our district has done community-wide surveys in the past," said Greg Bott, park district director. "The recreational opportunity with the highest demand was bicycling. And we are trying to respond to that."

Although the routes haven't been planned yet, one trail could be built along the DuPage River. If it were built, the path could connect Plainfield with Naperville, Joliet, and Bolingbrook, said John Vann, assistant director for parks and planning.

LOOK AHEAD TO

Chibi: A True Story from Japan

In the next story, a mother duck decides to raise her babies in a busy downtown park. Read and notice statements of fact and opinion about the choices the mother duck makes.

Vocabulary

Words to Know

avenue	pool	splash
ducklings	nest	spring

When you read, you may come across a word you don't know. To figure out its meaning, look for clues near it. A definition or an example given near the unknown word may be a clue.

Notice how *ducklings* is used in the paragraph. Look for a definition near it to find what it means.

No Place Like Home

Just like every spring, animals were getting ready to have babies. Mother Duck looked for a place to build a nest where she could raise her ducklings. The baby ducks needed a safe place to live. Mother Duck marched straight up the busy avenue, avoiding the cars. Splash! She landed in a pool in the park. She splashed happily, knowing she had found a home.

Write About It

Draw the duck family. Write a caption. Use some vocabulary words.

Chibi

A True Story from Japan

by Barbara Brenner and Julia Takaya

illustrated by June Otani

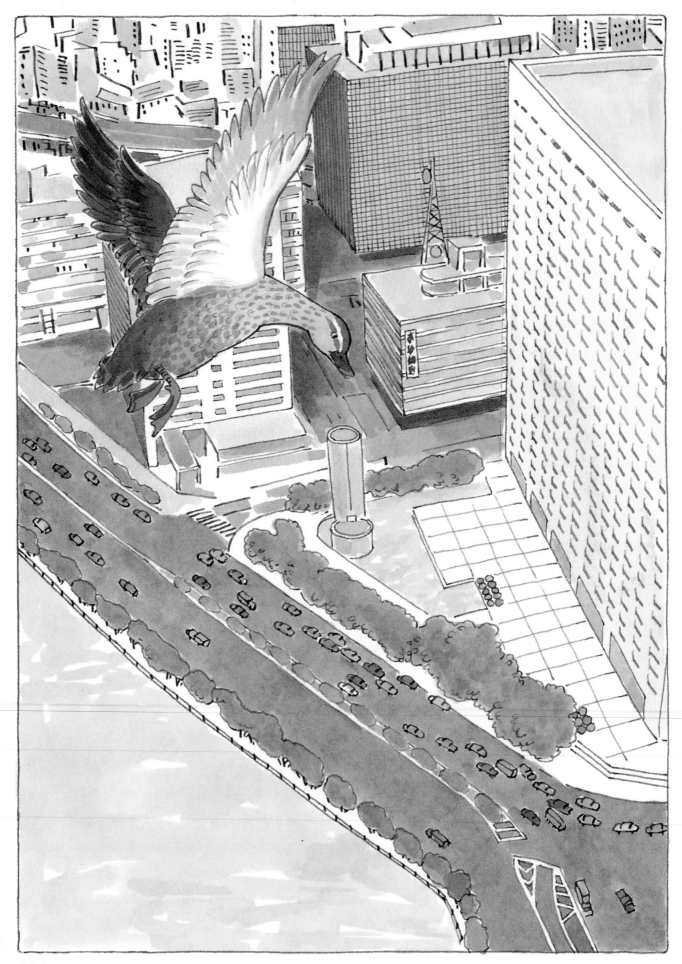

One spring morning a brown-and-gold duck flew over a skyscraper in Tokyo, Japan.

Far below her she spied a pool of water gleaming like glass. She dipped down and glided onto it, hardly making a splash. After a quick look around, the duck settled down in a clump of ivy by the pool and proceeded to build her nest.

It didn't seem to bother her that she was in an office park in downtown Tokyo . . . or that she was only a stone's throw away from Uchibori *Dori*, the eight-lane avenue where three hundred cars a minute roar in and out of the city. The duck went right on with her work.

Soon the nest held ten ivory-colored eggs. The *oka-san* brooded them herself, turning the eggs gently with her feet from time to time so they would keep warm on all sides.

Twenty-six days later there was a commotion in the ivy. One egg cracked, and a wet little baby duck pecked its way out of the shell. Then another egg hatched, then seven more. Within hours there were nine fluffy ducklings in the ivy, snuggled under their mother's warm brood feathers.

At exactly noon, the mother duck lifted her bill, stood up, and waggled her tail. Was the bill or the tail the signal? The ducklings gathered behind their mother—Chibi first, then the others. Marching single file, they followed Oka-san to the exit. But—wait! She wasn't leading them to where the watchers had gathered. Oka-san was heading for the *opposite* exit.

Sato-san was the first to realize what she meant to do. Frantically he dialed the police. Then, camera in hand, he clambered over the azalea bushes and raced along the divider to the other exit.

The street crossing light was changing from *midori* to *akai*—green to red. Oka-san ignored it. Looking straight ahead, she waddled down from the curb. Chibi and the other ducklings did the same. At that moment a sports car came speeding down the broad avenue. It was heading straight for the ducks. Sato-san, who was about to take a picture, dropped his camera and ran into the street. Waving his arms frantically, he shouted at the driver to stop. *"Tomatte! Tomatte!"*

The car swerved. Brakes screeched. Police whistles blew. Flashbulbs went off. But Oka-san paid no attention. Calmly she herded her brood across four lanes, up onto the divider, then down onto the remaining four lanes.

Predict

- To **predict** means to tell what you think might happen next in a story based on what has already happened.

- A prediction is what you say will happen.

- As you read, use what you know from your own life and from what you've learned and look for clues in the story that help you decide what might happen next.

Read "Keep the Buckets Coming" from *A Little Excitement* by Marc Harshman.

Talk About It

1. What clues from the story and from your own life helped you make your prediction?

2. How close was your prediction to what really happened?

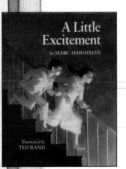

Keep the Buckets Coming

by Marc Harshman

A fire, set in the woodburning stove, has gotten out of hand.

. . . Side by side with Annie I worked, quietly and hard and quickly, to keep the buckets coming to Dad. Later I saw his hands bloody from fighting to keep a hold on that slippery roof. *Roar* and *whoosh* were the sounds the fire made, and I was more scared than excited. . . .

Eventually the Piney Volunteer Fire Department gathered: Jimmy up from Adeline, and Harry from Dutch Fork, Bob from Clouston, and Dan Creary from Sleepy Creek Hollow. They all came in pickups since the pump truck was frozen up solid over at Dixon's. Neighbors from across the valley and down the ridge would arrive, too, before it was over. But, of course, the first one there was Dad himself—he joked later that no one had ever been quicker than that to a fire, and if they had, he'd eat his Sunday pants.

> **Predict what will happen now that the volunteer fire department has arrived.**

The night was beautiful, all white and black beyond the fire. Somewhere in that black a deer must have lifted her nose from grass pawed clear of snow, looked over our way, and wondered—too smart and too quick to be scared. I felt better when I heard Jimmy and Bob, Harry and Dan shouting and laughing, even when it seemed they shouldn't. But finally we watched the orange flames fall back until one hour after it had started, Bob Jackson shone his flashlight down the flue and announced: "She's all gone, folks! Get on in the house and get to bed." And of course, we didn't. . . .

LOOK AHEAD TO

Brave Irene

In the next story, Irene must deliver the dress to the duchess on time. Will she be able to do it, or will the storm stop her? Read and predict what will happen.

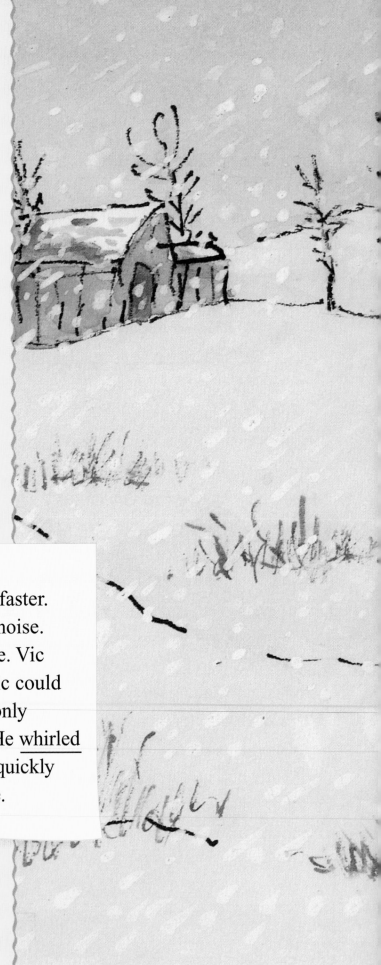

Vocabulary

Words to Know

howling   whipped   wind
snatched   whirled   stumble

Words that are spelled the same but pronounced differently are called **homographs.** Homographs also have different meanings. To know which meaning is correct look for clues in nearby sentences.

Read the paragraph. Decide if *wind* rhymes with *find* and means "go in a crooked way," or rhymes with *skinned* and means "air in motion."

Saving Sam

The wind was blowing stronger and faster. The wind's howling made a terrible noise. The flag whipped on the pole outside. Vic knew he had to find his dog Sam. Vic could barely walk in the wind—he could only stumble. Suddenly, he heard a bark. He whirled around to find Sam behind him. Vic quickly snatched Sam up and took him inside.

Talk About It

Use vocabulary words to discuss a storm you've seen or been in.

Brave Irene

written and illustrated by William Steig

Mrs. Bobbin, the dressmaker, was tired and had a bad headache, but she still managed to sew the last stitches in the gown she was making.

"It's the most beautiful dress in the whole world!" said her daughter, Irene. "The duchess will love it."

"It *is* nice," her mother admitted. "But, dumpling, it's for tonight's ball, and I don't have the strength to bring it. I feel sick."

"Poor Mama," said Irene. "I can get it there!"

"No, cupcake, I can't let you," said Mrs. Bobbin. "Such a huge package, and it's such a long way to the palace. Besides, it's starting to snow."

"But I *love* snow," Irene insisted. She coaxed her mother into bed, covered her with two quilts, and added a blanket for her feet. Then she fixed her some tea with lemon and honey and put more wood in the stove.

With great care, Irene took the splendid gown down from the dummy and packed it in a big box with plenty of tissue paper.

"Dress warmly, pudding," her mother called in a weak voice, "and don't forget to button up. It's cold out there, and windy."

Irene put on her fleece-lined boots, her red hat and muffler, her heavy coat, and her mittens. She kissed her mother's hot forehead six times, then once again, made sure she was tucked in snugly, and slipped out with the big box, shutting the door firmly behind her.

It really was cold outside, very cold. The wind whirled the falling snowflakes about, this way, that way, and into Irene's squinting face. She set out on the uphill path to Farmer Bennett's sheep pasture.

By the time she got there, the snow was up to her ankles and the wind was worse. It hurried her along and made her stumble. Irene resented this; the box was problem enough. "Easy does it!" she cautioned the wind, leaning back hard against it.

By the middle of the pasture, the flakes were falling thicker. Now the wind drove Irene along so rudely she had to hop, skip, and go helter-skeltering over the knobby ground. Cold snow sifted into her boots and chilled her feet. She pushed out her lip and hurried on. This was an important errand.

When she reached Apple Road, the wind decided to put on a show. It ripped branches from trees and flung them about, swept up and scattered the fallen snow, got in front of Irene to keep her from moving ahead. Irene turned around and pressed on backwards.

"Go home!" the wind squalled. "Irene . . . go hooooooome . . ."

"I will do no such thing," she snapped. "No such thing, you wicked wind!"

"Go ho—o—ome," the wind yodeled. "GO HO—WO—WOME," it shrieked, "or else." For a short second, Irene wondered if she shouldn't heed the wind's warning. But no! *The gown had to get to the duchess!*

The wind wrestled her for the package—walloped it, twisted it, shook it, snatched at it. But Irene wouldn't yield. "It's my mother's work!" she screamed.

Then—oh, woe!—the box was wrenched from her mittened grasp and sent bumbling along in the snow. Irene went after it.

She pounced and took hold, but the ill-tempered wind ripped the box open. The ball gown flounced out and went waltzing through the powdered air with tissue-paper attendants.

Irene clung to the empty box and watched the beautiful gown disappear.

How could anything so terribly wrong be allowed to happen? Tears froze on her lashes. Her dear mother's hard work, all those days of measuring, cutting, pinning, stitching . . . for *this?* And the poor duchess! Irene decided she would have to trudge on with just the box and explain everything in person.

She went shuffling through the snow. Would her mother understand, she wondered, that it was the wind's fault, not hers? Would the duchess be angry? The wind was howling like a wild animal.

Suddenly Irene stepped in a hole and fell over with a twisted ankle. She blamed it on the wind. "Keep quiet!" she scolded. "You've done enough damage already. You've spoiled everything! *Everything!*"

The wind swallowed up her words.

Irene pushed forward with all her strength and—*sloosh! thwump!*—she plunged downward and was buried. She had fallen off a little cliff. Only her hat and the box in her hands stuck out above the snow.

Even if she could call for help, no one would hear her. Her body shook. Her teeth chattered. Why not freeze to death, she thought, and let all these troubles end. Why not? She was already buried.

And never see her mother's face again? Her good mother who smelled like fresh-baked bread? In an explosion of fury, she flung her body about to free herself and was finally able to climb up on her knees and look around.

How to get down to that glittering palace? As soon as she raised the question, she had the answer.

She laid the box down and climbed aboard. But it pressed into the snow and stuck. She tried again, and this time, instead of climbing on, she leaped. The box shot forward, like a sled.

The wind raced after Irene but couldn't keep up. In a moment she would be with people again, inside where it was warm. The sled slowed and jerked to a stop on paving stones.

The time had come to break the bad news to the duchess. With the empty box clasped to her chest, Irene strode nervously toward the palace.

But then her feet stopped moving and her mouth fell open. She stared. Maybe this was impossible, yet there it was, a little way off and over to the right, hugging the trunk of a tree—the beautiful ball gown! The wind was holding it there.

"Mama!" Irene shouted. "Mama, I found it!"

She managed somehow, despite the wind's meddling, to get the gown off the tree and back in its box. And in another moment she was at the door of the palace. She knocked twice with the big brass knocker. The door opened and she burst in.

She was welcomed by cheering servants and a
delirious duchess. They couldn't believe she had
come over the mountain in such a storm, all by
herself. She had to tell the whole story, every
detail. And she did.

Then she asked to be taken right back to her sick
mother. But it was out of the question, they said; the
road that ran around the mountain wouldn't be
cleared till morning.

"Don't fret, child," said the duchess. "Your
mother is surely sleeping now. We'll get you there
first thing tomorrow."

Irene was given a good dinner as she sat by
the fire, the moisture steaming off her clothes. The
duchess, meanwhile, got into her freshly ironed gown
before the guests began arriving in their sleighs.

What a wonderful ball it was! The duchess in her new gown was like a bright star in the sky. Irene in her ordinary dress was radiant. She was swept up into dances by handsome aristocrats, who kept her feet off the floor to spare her ankle. Her mother would enjoy hearing all about it.

Early the next morning, when snow had long since ceased falling, Mrs. Bobbin woke from a good night's sleep feeling much improved. She hurried about and got a fire going in the cold stove. Then she went to look in on Irene.

But Irene's bed was empty! She ran to the window and gazed at the white landscape. No one out there. Snow powder fell from the branch of a tree.

"Where is my child?" Mrs. Bobbin cried. She whipped on her coat to go out and find her.

When she pulled the door
open, a wall of drift faced her.
But peering over it, she could see
a horse-drawn sleigh hastening up
the path. And seated on the sleigh,
between two large footmen, was
Irene herself, asleep but smiling.

Would you like to hear the rest?

Well, there was a bearded doctor in the back of the
sleigh. And the duchess had sent Irene's mother a
ginger cake with white icing, some oranges and a
pineapple, and spice candy of many flavors, along
with a note saying how much she cherished her
gown, and what a brave and loving person Irene was.

Which, of course, Mrs. Bobbin knew. Better than
the duchess.

About the Author/Illustrator
William Steig

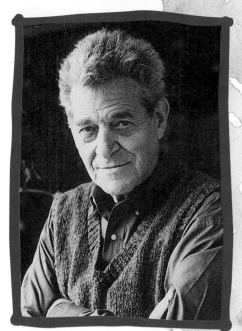

William Steig has created many wonderful stories. How does he start? "First of all I decide it's time to write a story," he says. "Then I say, 'What shall I draw this time? A pig or a mouse?' Or, 'I did a pig last time; I'll make it a mouse this time.' Then I start drawing."

When Mr. Steig was young, the Depression hit his family hard, and they lost all of their money. Since Mr. Steig's brothers were either married or too young to earn a living, it was up to him to help the family. "The only thing I could do was draw," he says. "Within a year I was selling cartoons to the *New Yorker* [magazine] and supporting a family." He drew cartoons for many years before a co-worker suggested he try creating a children's book.

Mr. Steig finds illustrating a book a lot harder than just drawing pictures. He says, "I love to draw, and I love to write—but I hate to illustrate. When you draw, you draw anything that wants to come out, but when you illustrate you have to draw someone who has on a polka-dot dress. It has to be the same as the previous picture. You have to remember what it says in the story."

Reader Response

Open for Discussion

If you were playing a game, would you like
to have Irene on your team? Why or why not?

Comprehension Check

1. Tell two events in the story that show how much
Irene cares about her mother.

2. Why is it important to Irene to get the gown to the
duchess? Is that a good enough reason for Irene to
take the risks she takes?

3. Both Irene and Charles Lindbergh are brave. What
other qualities do they share?

4. As you were reading, what did you **predict** would
happen when Irene first went out into the blizzard?
On what did you base your prediction?

5. As you were reading, what did you **predict** would
happen when Irene got to the castle? On what did
you base your prediction?

Ask the Artist

Look again at the pictures for *Brave Irene.* Then make a
list of questions you would like to ask the artist. Share
your questions with classmates.

Water on Earth

WHEN IS IT GOING TO RAIN?

from Grade 3, Scott Foresman *Discover the Wonder* Science Program

Notice the clouds in the picture below. If you saw these clouds, would you want to get out your umbrella or boots? You might. Dark clouds often bring rain.

RAINING AND SLEETING

Water vapor rises into the cool air high above the earth. Then the water vapor condenses on invisible bits of dust and salt in the air, forming droplets. Clouds are made of billions of these tiny droplets.

What happens to water droplets high in the air where temperatures are below freezing? If you said that water droplets freeze into bits of ice, you're right.

Water droplets keep freezing onto the ice bits, making them larger and larger. The bits of ice become too heavy to float in the air. Then these bits of ice fall down through the clouds. They fall to the ground as snowflakes.

Reading Across Texts

Reading a Science Textbook Article

✓ **Read the titles.** They tell you the big idea of the selection.

✓ **Look at the subtitles.** They tell you the main idea of each part of the selection.

✓ **Look at the graphic sources and little features.** Graphs, charts, pictures, and captions help you understand the selection better.

✓ **Read the questions at the end.** They help you think about what you have learned. Reread to make sure your answers are correct.

Focus Your Reading

After you read "Water on Earth," compare it to *Brave Irene*. Would Irene's journey have been easier in rainy weather? Why do you think as you do?

CLOUDS OFTEN GET DARK BEFORE A STORM.

209

How Big Is a Raindrop?

In the tropics, near the Equator, the air is very warm. So most clouds in the tropics are made of tiny water droplets, but not bits of ice. A drop of water in a cloud is very tiny, but not as small as a speck of dust.

WIDTH (IN MM)

SMALLEST RAINDROP 200/1000

CLOUD DROPLET 100/1000

DUST PARTICLE 1/1000

Rain will only fall if the cloud droplets join and become at least as large as the small raindrop shown above. The average raindrop is much bigger and is made of many cloud droplets.

What Did You Find Out?

1. How wide is a cloud droplet?
2. Do you think you could see one cloud droplet? Why?
3. How many times wider is the small raindrop than the cloud droplet?

Water in any form that falls from clouds is called **precipitation** (pri sip′ ə tā′ shən). Snow is one kind of precipitation that you may have seen.

Suppose the air temperatures near the ground are above freezing. Would snowflakes fall? You probably figured out that warm air makes ice melt. That's right. In warmer temperatures, the bits of ice that fall from the clouds melt into raindrops. Rain is another kind of precipitation.

Suppose raindrops pass through a thick layer of very cold air close to the earth. These raindrops freeze before they can fall. This kind of precipitation is called sleet. You can even hear sleet rattle when it hits the ground!

THE WATER CYCLE

The rainstorm finally is over. You see puddles of water everywhere. You might even feel like splashing in a puddle like this child is doing.

WHAT MIGHT HAPPEN TO THIS PUDDLE? IT MIGHT EVAPORATE.

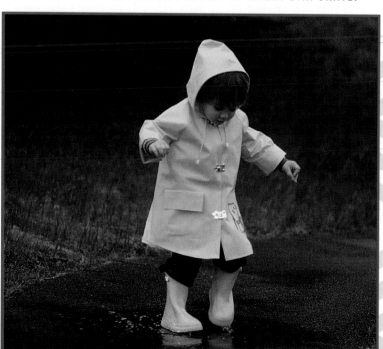

The sky looks clear now. Suddenly, the sun begins shining brightly. Later, you notice that the puddles have disappeared.

What happened to the water in the puddles? Let's review what you learned in Module A. Light energy from the sun causes the water to evaporate. The water vapor can condense into water droplets, forming clouds. These water droplets can freeze. What happens when bits of ice in clouds become too heavy to stay in the air? You already learned the answer to that question. Precipitation falls from the clouds.

The process of evaporation, condensation, and precipitation is called the **water cycle.** Trace the three steps of the water cycle shown in the picture. The entire water cycle keeps repeating itself over and over again.

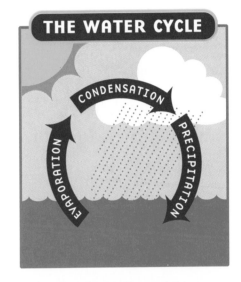

THE WATER CYCLE

CONDENSATION
PRECIPITATION
EVAPORATION

INTO THE FIELD

What do clouds look like?

Go outside and observe clouds once a day for two weeks. Record what you see. Describe how the clouds are alike and different.

CHECKPOINT

1. How do rain and snow form?

2. What are the steps in the water cycle?

3. **Take Action!** Place a small mirror into a freezer for a few minutes. Remove the mirror and breathe on it. What forms on the mirror? Explain why.

Author's Purpose

- The **author's purpose** is the author's reason for writing.

- An author may try to express or to describe something in a way that gives the reader a feeling about or sets the mood of the scene.

- Another purpose is that an author may try to entertain the reader.

Read "Tomás Visits the Library" from *Tomás and the Library Lady* **by Pat Mora.**

Talk About It

1. What mood or feeling did you get as you read about Tomás?

2. How does the author give you this feeling?

Tomás
Visits the Library
by Pat Mora

Tomás stood in front of the library doors. He pressed his nose against the glass and peeked in. The library was huge!

A hand tapped his shoulder. Tomás jumped. A tall lady looked down at him. "It's a hot day," she said. "Come inside and have a drink of water. What's your name?" she asked.

"Tomás," he said.

"Come, Tomás," she said.

Inside it was cool. Tomás had never seen so many books. The lady watched him. "Come," she said again, leading him to a drinking fountain. "First some water. Then I will bring

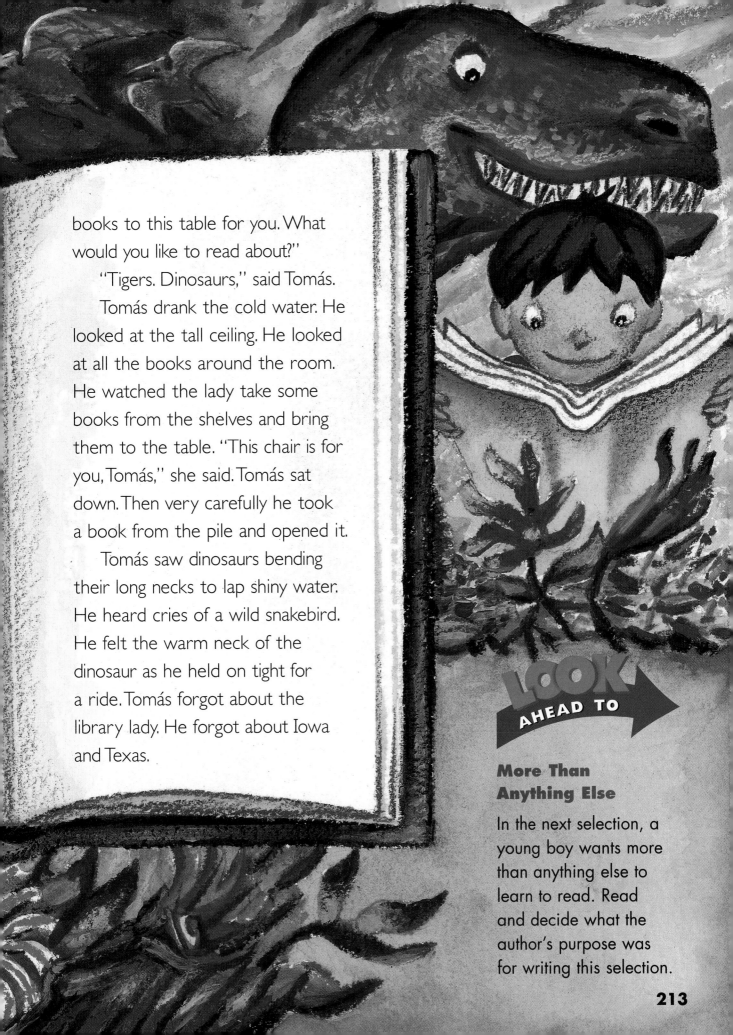

books to this table for you. What would you like to read about?"

"Tigers. Dinosaurs," said Tomás.

Tomás drank the cold water. He looked at the tall ceiling. He looked at all the books around the room. He watched the lady take some books from the shelves and bring them to the table. "This chair is for you, Tomás," she said. Tomás sat down. Then very carefully he took a book from the pile and opened it.

Tomás saw dinosaurs bending their long necks to lap shiny water. He heard cries of a wild snakebird. He felt the warm neck of the dinosaur as he held on tight for a ride. Tomás forgot about the library lady. He forgot about Iowa and Texas.

LOOK AHEAD TO

More Than Anything Else

In the next selection, a young boy wants more than anything else to learn to read. Read and decide what the author's purpose was for writing this selection.

Words to Know

alphabet   magic   cabin
newspaper   learning   tales

Words that are pronounced the same but spelled differently, such as *tales* and *tails,* are called **homophones.** Homophones also have different meanings. To understand the difference between them, look for clues in nearby sentences.

Read the paragraph. Why is the word *tales* used below and not *tails?*

A Good Lesson to Learn

I grew up in a <u>cabin</u>. To get the job I wanted, I needed to read. So I started by <u>learning</u> the letters of the <u>alphabet</u>. Then, almost as if by <u>magic</u>, I could read whole words! I could even read articles in a <u>newspaper</u>. I learned to read and write so well that I have written some best-selling <u>tales</u>!

Write About It

What has been hard for you to learn? Write a journal entry about it. Use some vocabulary words.

More Than Anything Else

by Marie Bradby / illustrated by Chris K. Soentpiet

I see a man reading a newspaper aloud and all doubt falls away. I have found hope, and it is as brown as me.

I see myself the man. And as I watch his eyes move
across the paper, it is as if *I* know what the black
marks mean, as if *I* am reading. As if everyone is
listening to *me*. And I hold that thought in my hands.

I will work until I am the best reader in the county. Children will crowd around me, and I will teach *them* to read.

But Papa taps me on the shoulder. "Come on." And John tugs at my shirt. They don't see what I see. They don't see what I can be.

We hurry home. "Mama, I have to learn to read,"
I say. She holds my hand and feels my
hunger racing fast as my heart.

It is a small book—a blue the color of midnight.
She gives it to me one evening in the corner of our
cabin, pulling it from under the clothes that she
washes and irons to make a little money.

She doesn't say where she got it. She can't read
it herself. But she knows this is something called
the alphabet. She thinks it is a sing-y kind of
thing. A song on paper.

After work, even though my shoulders still ache
and my legs are stained with salt, I study my book.
I stare at the marks and try to imagine their song.

I draw the marks on the dirt floor and try to figure out what sounds they make, what story their picture tells.

But sometimes I feel I am trying to jump without legs. And my thoughts get slippery, and I can't keep up with what I want to be, and how good I will feel when I learn this magic, and how people will look up to me.

I can't catch the tune of what I see. I get a salt-shoveling pain and feel my dreams are slipping away.

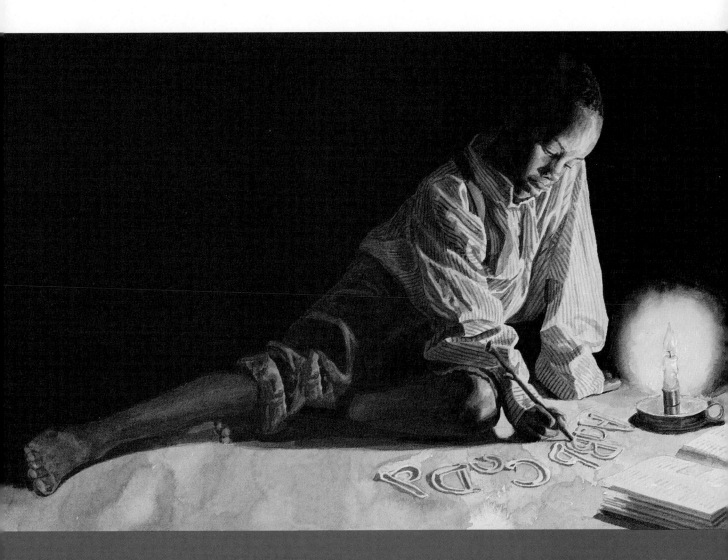

I have got to find him—that newspaper man.
I look everywhere.
Finally, I find that brown face of hope.

He tells me the song—the sounds the marks make.
I jump up and down singing it. I shout and
laugh like when I was baptized in the creek.
I have jumped into another world and I am saved.

But I have to know more. "Tell me more," I say.
"What's your name?" he asks.
"Booker," I say.

And he takes the sound of my name and draws
it on the ground.

I linger over that picture. I know I can hold it
forever.

About the Author

Marie Bradby

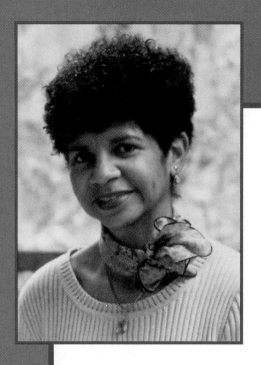

More Than Anything Else is Marie Bradby's first children's book. She has also worked as a newspaper reporter and written articles for *National Geographic* magazine. She lives in Louisville, Kentucky, with her family.

About the Illustrator

Chris K. Soentpiet

Chris K. Soentpiet came to the United States from Korea when he was eight years old. Before he created the pictures for the book *More Than Anything Else,* he visited the Booker T. Washington National Monument in Hardy, Virginia. He studied the life of Booker T. Washington. When he made the pictures of young Booker and his family, Mr. Soentpiet wanted to make sure the pictures were true to life.

Open for Discussion

What would you say to nine-year-old Booker if you could join him in one of the pictures? How might you help him?

Comprehension Check

1. Why didn't Booker learn to read in school as many children today do?

2. How do you think the newspaper man learned to read?

3. From the story, you can tell that Booker's family is poor. Find details in the story that support this conclusion.

4. The **author's purpose** is the writer's reason for writing. Give one important purpose the author might have had for writing about Booker. Why do you think this?

5. Often an **author** has more than one **purpose** for writing. Give another reason the author might have had for writing about Booker. Why do you think so?

The Real Booker

Part of this biography is made up, but there really was a Booker. Use an encyclopedia to find out what Booker T. Washington did when he grew up. Share your facts with the class.

Plot

- A story's **plot** includes the important events that happen in the beginning, middle, and end of a story.

- Look for events that are important to the plot. They help keep the story going.

- A story map can help you keep track of the most important events in a story.

Read "Chiefy Stays Over" from *Popsicle Pony* **by Jill Stover.**

Write About It

1. Make a story map with a classmate. Write *beginning* at the top of a piece of paper, *middle* in the middle of the paper, and *end* near the bottom of the paper.

2. Write important events that happen in each part of the story. Share your map.

Chiefy Stays Over

by Jill Stover

A girl decides to help out the owner of a pony-drawn ice cream wagon by taking care of his pony, Chiefy.

One evening Popsicle Pete didn't come. He was sick and had to go to the hospital for a few days. Chiefy came to stay with me. My backyard became a real Texas ranch, and I turned into a real Texas cowgirl.

Every morning I tried to ride Chiefy over to the hospital to see Popsicle Pete. And every morning he refused to go. I coaxed him with carrots. I bribed him with cookies. I even tried chili peppers. But Chiefy was stubborn, and I didn't know how to handle him. He wouldn't budge.

I went out to try one more time. The yard was empty. Chiefy had escaped. Pretty soon we got a call from the county sheriff. Chiefy was in big trouble.

After his great escape, he had taken his regular route through town. First he went to the Moo-Moo to get a special treat. Then he went past the Longhorn Feed Store for another little something. Finally he stopped at the Twin Dophins Movie Theater for one more snack. The movie must have been pretty exciting, because Chiefy decided to stay. But he raised a ruckus, and the manager called in the sheriff.

When he was arrested, Chiefy trotted happily along his regular route to the county jail, where he was locked in a cell to keep him out of any more trouble.

LOOK AHEAD TO

Leah's Pony

In the next story, Leah is proud of her pony. All seems fine until real trouble starts. Read and see what important events happen in the beginning, middle, and end of the story.

Vocabulary

Words to Know

chores   pasture   sturdy
pony   swift   dust
saddle

Words with similar meanings, such as *happy* and *joyful,* are **synonyms.** You can often figure out the meaning of an unknown word by looking for a clue around it. This clue is sometimes a synonym.

Read the paragraph. Notice how *jobs* helps you understand *chores.*

Work Some, Play Some

Lucia watched the dust blowing around the cornfields, but weeding was one of the many jobs she had to do. Only after her chores were done could she play. As she worked, Lucia thought of her pony Freckles. She saw the sturdy, swift animal out in the pasture running here and there. She couldn't wait to get into the saddle and ride him again.

Talk About It

What things would you like to do on a farm? Tell a friend. Use as many vocabulary words as you can.

Leah's Pony

written by Elizabeth Friedrich

illustrated by Michael Garland

Leah wanted to run away. She raced her pony
past empty fields lined with dry gullies. She
galloped past a house with rags stuffed in broken
windowpanes. She sped right past Mr. B. sweeping
the steps outside his store.

At last Leah knew what she had to do. She
turned her pony around and rode back into town.

She stopped in front of Mr. B.'s store. "You can buy my pony," she said.

Mr. B. stopped sweeping and stared at her. "Why would you want to sell him?" he asked. "That's the finest pony in the county."

Leah swallowed hard. "I've grown a lot this summer," she said. "I'm getting too big for him."

Sunburned soil crunched under Leah's feet as she walked home alone. The auction had begun. Neighbors, friends, strangers—everyone clustered around the man in the big hat. "How much for this wagon?" boomed the man. "Five dollars. Ten dollars. Sold for fifteen dollars to the man in the green shirt."

Papa's best bull.

Sold.

Mama's prize rooster.

Sold.

Leah's favorite calf.

Sold.

Leah clutched her money in her hand. "It has to be enough," she whispered to herself. "It just has to be."

"Here's one of the best items in this entire auction," yelled the man in the big hat. "Who'll start the bidding at five hundred dollars for this practically new, all-purpose Farmall tractor? It'll plow, plant, fertilize, and even cultivate for you."

It was time. Leah's voice shook. "One dollar."

The man in the big hat laughed. "That's a low starting bid if I ever heard one," he said. "Now let's hear some serious bids."

No one moved. No one said a word. No one even seemed to breathe.

"Ladies and gentlemen, this tractor is a beauty! I have a bid of only one dollar for it. One dollar for this practically new Farmall tractor! Do I hear any other bids?"

Again no one moved. No one said a word. No one even seemed to breathe.

"This is ridiculous!" the man's voice boomed out from under his hat into the silence. "Sold to the young lady for one dollar."

The crowd cheered. Papa's mouth hung open. Mama cried. Leah proudly walked up and handed one dollar to the auctioneer in the big hat.

"That young lady bought one fine tractor for one very low price," the man continued. "Now how much am I bid for this flock of healthy young chickens?"

"I'll give you ten cents," offered a farmer who lived down the road.

"Ten cents! Ten cents is mighty cheap for a whole flock of chickens," the man said. His face looked angry.

Again no one moved. No one said a word. No one even seemed to breathe.

"Sold for ten cents!"

The farmer picked up the cage filled with chickens and walked over to Mama. "These chickens are yours," he said.

The man pushed his big hat back on his head. "How much for this good Ford pickup truck?" he asked.

"Twenty-five cents," yelled a neighbor from town.

Again no one moved. No one said a word. No one even seemed to breathe.

"Sold for twenty-five cents!" The man in the big hat shook his head. "This isn't supposed to be a penny auction!" he shouted.

The neighbor paid his twenty-five cents and took the keys to the pickup truck. "I think these will start your truck," he whispered as he dropped the keys into Papa's shirt pocket.

Leah watched as friends and neighbors bid a penny for a chicken or a nickel for a cow or a quarter for a plow. One by one, they gave everything back to Mama and Papa.

The crowds left. The sign disappeared. Chickens scratched in their coop, and cattle called for their corn. The farm was quiet. Too quiet. No familiar whinny greeted Leah when she entered the barn. Leah swallowed hard and straightened her back.

That night in Leah's hushed house, no sad voices whispered in the kitchen. Only Leah lay awake, listening to the clock chime nine and even ten times. Leah's heart seemed to copy its slow, sad beat.

The next morning Leah forced open the heavy barn doors to start her chores. A loud whinny greeted her. Leah ran and hugged the familiar furry neck and kissed the white snip of a nose. "You're back!" she cried. "How did you get here?"

Then Leah saw the note with her name written in big letters:

Dear Leah,

This is the finest pony in the county. But he's a little bit small for me and a little bit big for my grandson.

He fits you much better.

Your friend,

Mr. B.

P.S. I heard how you saved your family's farm. These hard times won't last forever.

And they didn't.

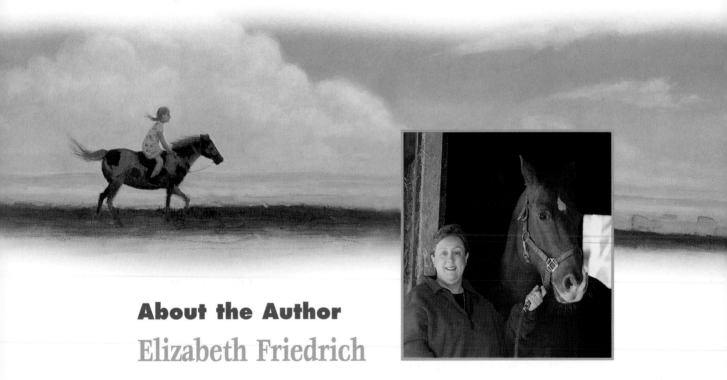

About the Author
Elizabeth Friedrich

Elizabeth Friedrich knows what farm life is like. She lives in Stratham, New Hampshire, with her husband and her two children. They share their farm with six sheep and a horse named Tuffy.

Open for Discussion

Pretend you are Leah telling your grandchildren about the pony you once owned and the hard times you lived through.

Comprehension Check

1. Why did Leah offer only one dollar for the tractor?

2. "Hard times" are an important part of the setting of the story. What are some details that make that time come to life for you?

3. How does the picture on page 245 help you know how brave Leah is?

4. Write the three most important events of the **plot** that tell the beginning, middle, and end of the story.

5. Which of these events is more important to the **plot** of *Leah's Pony?* Tell why.

- The neighbors pack up and leave.
- Leah sells her pony.

What Am I Bid?

Work in a small group to make the auction scene into a play. Add more dialogue if you like and if it fits the overall scene. Then act out your auction.

At the Library
by Nikki Grimes

I flip the pages of a book and slip inside,
where crystal seas await and pirates hide.
I find a paradise where birds can talk,
where children fly and trees prefer to walk.
Sometimes I end up on a city street.
I recognize the brownskin girl I meet.
She's skinny, but she's strong, and brave, and wise.
I smile because I see me in her eyes.

A Book
by Myra Cohn Livingston

Closed, I am a mystery.
Open, I will always be
a friend with whom you think and see.

Closed, there's nothing I can say.
Open, we can dream and stray
to other worlds, far and away.

Somewhere

by Leland B. Jacobs

Where, oh where,
Can somewhere be?
In outer space?
Beneath the sea?

Is somewhere
Always far away?
In other lands?
Beyond today?

Is somewhere
Always farther still?
Beyond the woods,
Beyond the hill?

It's difficult
To be aware
Of somewhere else
Until you're there.

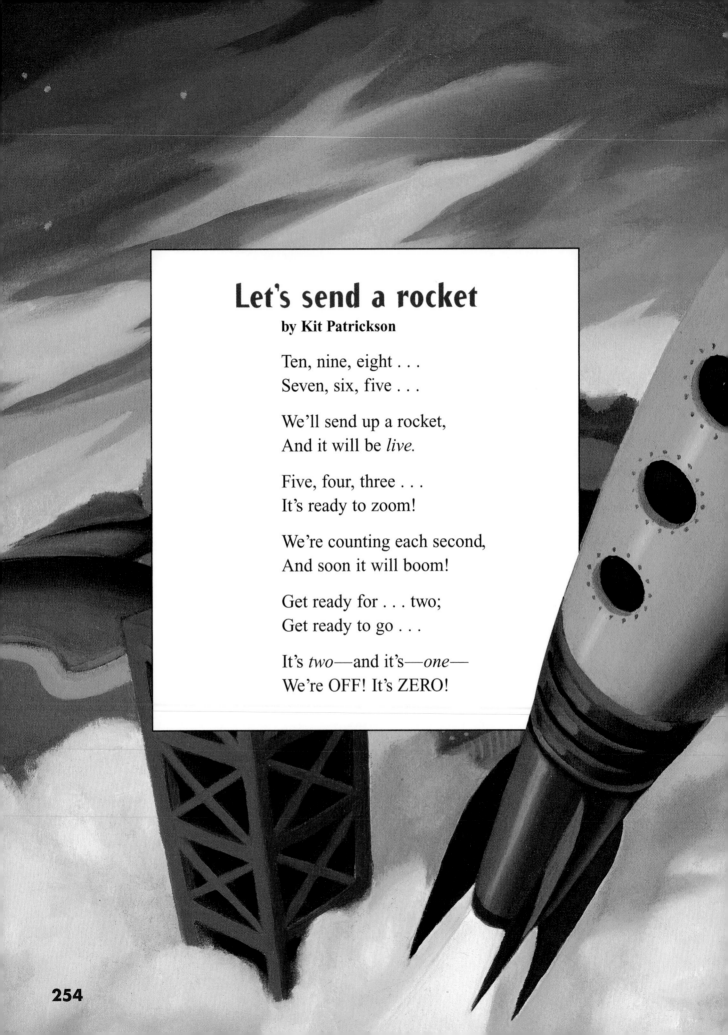

Let's send a rocket

by Kit Patrickson

Ten, nine, eight . . .
Seven, six, five . . .

We'll send up a rocket,
And it will be *live*.

Five, four, three . . .
It's ready to zoom!

We're counting each second,
And soon it will boom!

Get ready for . . . two;
Get ready to go . . .

It's *two*—and it's—*one*—
We're OFF! It's ZERO!

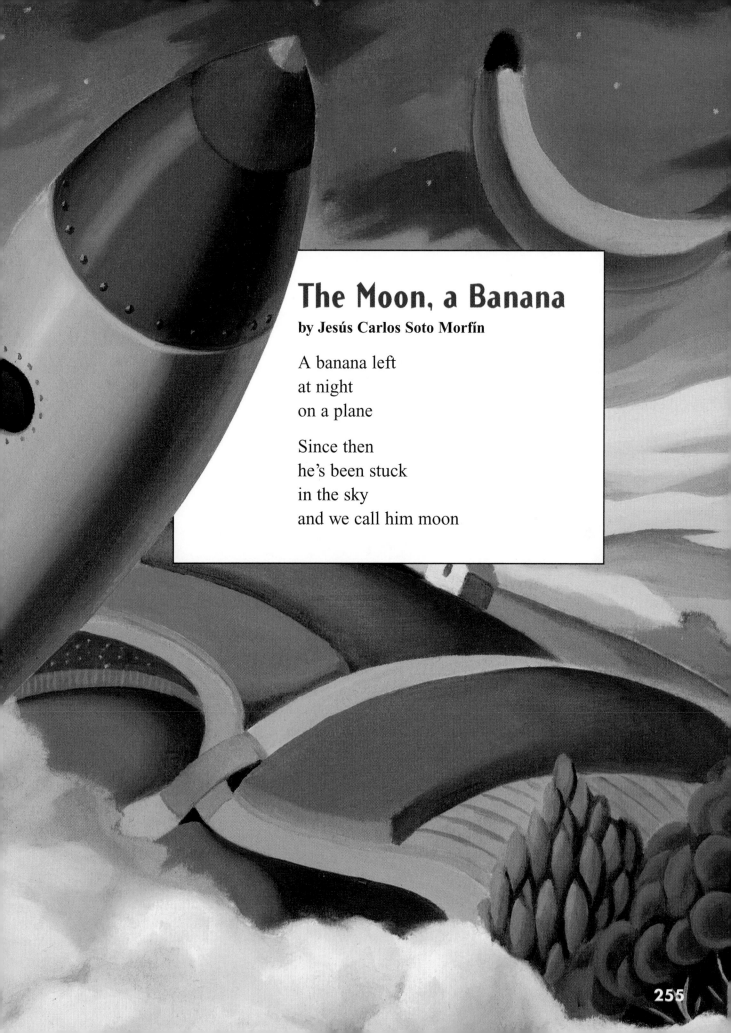

The Moon, a Banana

by Jesús Carlos Soto Morfín

A banana left
at night
on a plane

Since then
he's been stuck
in the sky
and we call him moon

Unit 6

kids

Imagination.kids

How many ways
can we use our
imaginations?

Skill Lesson

Steps in a Process

- Following **steps in a process** usually means doing or making something in a certain order. The steps might show the best way to make or do something.

- Sometimes the steps are given in pictures as well as words.

- Sometimes there are clue words, such as *the next step* or *then,* that help you with the order of the steps.

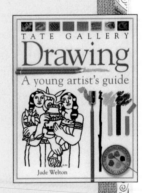

Read "Revealing a Pattern" from *Drawing: A Young Artist's Guide* by Jude Welton.

Talk About It

1. Each numbered step in "Revealing a Pattern" has more than one direction. Why do you think the author wrote the steps this way?

2. Do you think it would be easier to make each step one statement? Why or why not?

Revealing a Pattern
by Jude Welton

You can find patterns all around you, in both natural objects such as feathers, leaves, and shells, and manufactured objects, like fabrics, tiles, and carpets. Even your own skin has a pattern if you look closely. Sometimes a pattern is made up of lines only and sometimes it is made up of different colored shapes. Every object has its own texture, too, which you can see as well as touch. Think about the way patterns and textures combine on the surface of objects, and how you can use these combinations in your drawings.

Find a leaf with a strong vein pattern. You can make a copy of it by taking a rubbing.

1. Place the leaf smooth side down. Lay a sheet of paper over the leaf and rub over it firmly with a wax crayon. Its outline and the pattern of the veins should come clear.

258

2. Use different colored crayons to make leaf rubbings all over the paper. Go over the lines with colored pencil to strengthen the pattern.

3. You can brush a thin coat of watercolor over your repeat design. The wax crayon will hold off the watercolor so that the full leaf pattern stands out against the background.

LOOK AHEAD TO

The Piñata Maker

In the next story, Tío Rico makes piñatas for a living. Read and follow the steps as he turns paper into a beautiful swan.

Vocabulary

Words to Know

| cone | swan | famous |
| designed | creating | paste |

Many words have more than one meaning. To decide which meaning of a word is being used, look for clues in the surrounding sentences.

Read the paragraph below. Decide if *cone* means "an object with a flat, round base and pointed top" or "a scaly growth that bears the seeds on many evergreen trees."

Designing Decorations

I designed a beautiful swan out of papier-mâché for a party decoration. Creating the graceful long-necked bird was easy. I mixed sticky paste with water and soaked newspaper strips in it. Then I formed the newspaper strips into a cone. Finally, I shaped the cone into a swan. Maybe someday I will be famous for my creations!

Write About It

Write directions for a craft project that you enjoy. Use as many vocabulary words as you can.

260

The Piñata Maker

written and photographed

by George Ancona

Don Ricardo is seventy-seven years old. He
started creating piñatas fifteen years ago when
his former job, making felt sombreros, became
too hard for him. "I went to school," he says.
"But I didn't learn very much. I liked to go to the
river and play with my friends until one of our
fathers would discover us and chase us back to
school. My father was a hatter, and I left school
to help him. After I married I started my own
hat business.

"I think that working all those years in front of the hot fire gave me the rheumatism," he continues, moving about the house with the help of a cane. "It gave me the money to build this house brick by brick, but it also made it hard for me to walk."

Don Ricardo starts his day by making paste in the kitchen. He puts a small handful of flour into an old pot, adds enough water to make a thin paste, and breaks apart the lumps with his fingers. He adds kindling to the fire and fans it until the flames leap up. Then he puts the pot on the fire and stirs the mixture until it thickens. "Starch makes a better paste than flour," says Don Ricardo, "but it is scarce in town and very expensive."

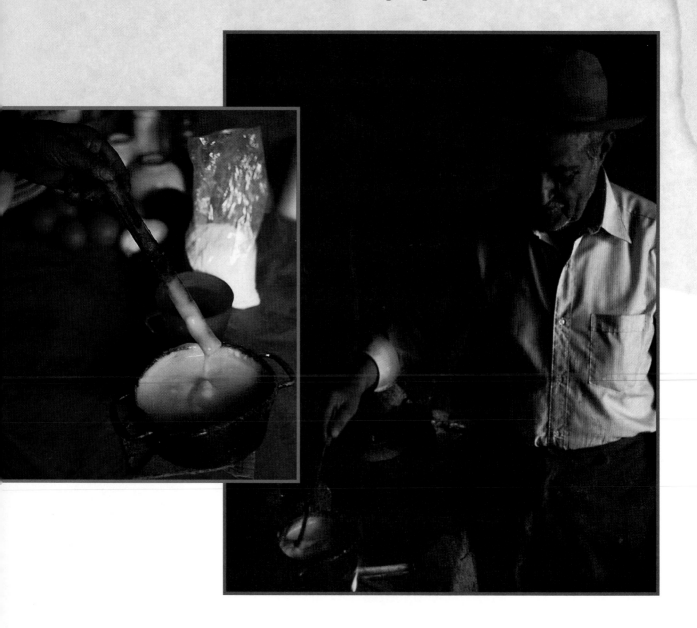

Today Tío Rico is making a piñata in the shape of a swan. He begins by rolling dry banana leaves into a thick rod with a bulge at one end for the head. He wraps the rod in brown paper smeared with paste. Then he forms the neck into an S-shaped curve and places it in the sun. Old irons hold it in shape until it's dry.

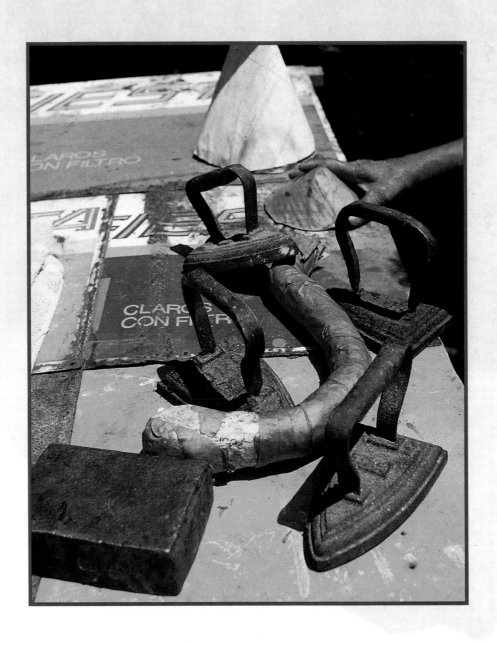

He paints the beak yellow and the feet orange.
After pasting the feet into position, Tío Rico adds
more feathers to the body and wings of the swan.

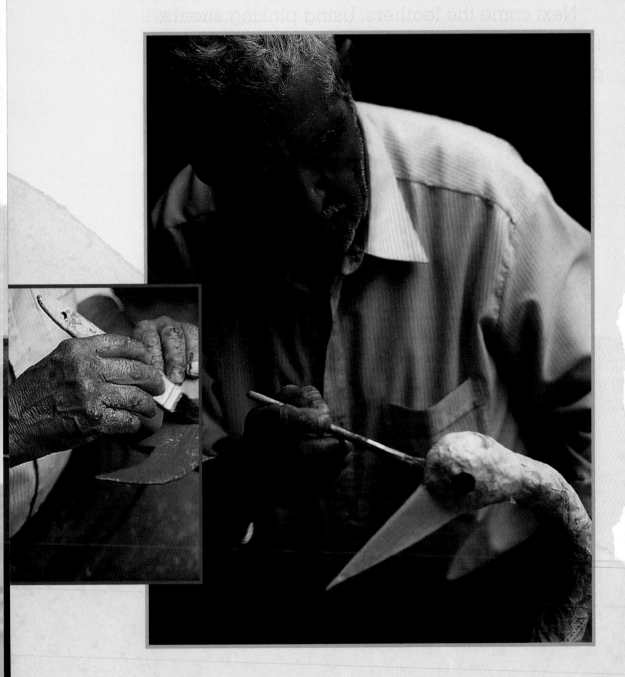

When everything is dry, Tío Rico uses a nail to
poke two small holes through the wings and the
pot. With a large needle and strong thread, he
secures the wings to the body.

Tío Rico covers the knotted threads with more white crepe paper feathers and holds up the swan for inspection. "Well," he says, pleased with his work, "let's see who will break this one."

Another of Tío Rico's famous piñatas is ready for a fiesta.

A Note from the Author/Photographer
George Ancona

My children, Lisa, Gina, Tomás, Isabel, Marina, and Pablo, all enjoyed breaking piñatas at their parties. We did not have a market where we could buy pots to make the piñatas, so we used cardboard boxes, which we made into shapes and then covered with paper. You can also use inflated balloons covered with papier-mâché. When the paper is dry, paint it, then cut a hole to fill the piñata with goodies.

273

Setting

- The **setting** is the time and place of a story.

- An author may not always tell you when and where a story takes place. Look for clues in the art or words that point to the setting of a story.

- The setting can have an effect on how a character acts in a story.

Read "On the Train" from *Bonanza Girl* by Patricia Beatty.

Talk About It

1. When do you think this story takes place? Why do you think so?

2. Does the setting have any effect on how the main character acts? Why do you think this way?

On the Train

by Patricia Beatty

When train time was called, we marched right past the bulging eyes of the ticket agent and took our places in the railroad car. "Well, we're on our way, children," Mama called. "You try to sleep as much as you can, so we won't be too tired when we come to Spokane Falls, and Jemmy, you keep away from doors and the stove and kerosene lamps, and do obey the conductor."

While Mama gave Jemmy instructions he certainly had no intention of following, I looked around the railroad car and sighed. It was like every other car I'd ever seen. The seats were hard and uncomfortable and about as slick as an icy hill, and every time I squirmed a little I nearly fell off into the aisle. There were kerosene lanterns hanging from the roof, and there was a coal and wood stove at the opposite end of the car. I took off my bonnet and gloves, placed my traveling cloak on the back of the seat, and settled down as best I could.

The train followed the Columbia River, and we stared out the windows at the great rock cliffs and waterfalls, but once we left the banks of the river, there was almost nothing to see. We rode for miles and miles and hours and hours, and saw nothing at all but dry prairie land, spotted here and there with sagebrush and sand dunes. When we came to a dusty little place called Wallula, we all switched to a new Northern Pacific line, finished two years before. While our baggage was moved, Mama, Jemmy, and I crossed the tracks along with the other passengers to have a cup of tea at a dusty little restaurant.

LOOK AHEAD TO

Mailing May

In the next story, May wants to go visit her grandmother in another part of the state. Read and see if you can tell when and where this story takes place.

279

Vocabulary

Words to Know

bundled	label	mailing
conductor	carted	station

Many words have more than one meaning. To decide which meaning of a word is being used, look for clues in nearby sentences.

Read the paragraph below. Decide if *conductor* means "a thing that transmits heat" or "a person in charge of a train and its passengers."

A Package for Larry

I like <u>mailing</u> packages to my brother Larry, who lives across the country. I <u>bundled</u> some cookies and put them in a box. Then I attached a <u>label</u> with Larry's address. My mom drove me to the train <u>station</u>. I watched as a forklift <u>carted</u> my package with hundreds of others to a waiting train. With the packages loaded, the <u>conductor</u>, the man in charge, signaled, and the cookies were on their way!

Talk About It

Imagine you are a package. Describe your journey from one place to another. Use vocabulary words.

MAILING MAY

MICHAEL O. TUNNELL

ILLUSTRATED BY

TED RAND

Then they made me go to bed awful early, which I did not like at all.

Next morning Ma shook me awake while it was still real dark. I was puzzled to see Pa's little traveling bag, packed and standing by the door. When I asked where he was going, Ma only smiled and said, "Eat your breakfast."

Just then someone knocked on our front door. Pa opened up to Ma's cousin Leonard.

"Come along, May," Pa said, grabbing the suitcase as Ma helped me with my coat. "We're going to the post office with Leonard." He held up his hand as I opened my mouth. "No questions," Pa said with a wink.

Ma hugged and kissed me before Pa took my hand and led me out into the dark winter air.

Before long I stood taking in the funny smells of the Grangeville post office: glue and canvas bags and oiled wooden floors. Meanwhile, Pa marched right up to Postmaster Perkins and said, "Sam, you got some new rules for mailing packages. I know boxes can weigh up to fifty pounds nowadays. But what sorts of things can you send?"

Mr. Perkins looked at Pa real strange-like as he asked, "What you got in mind, John?"

"It's May," said Pa. "We'd like to mail her to Lewiston. Leonard here mans the mail car on the train, as you well know. He can take good care of our package."

285

"Sure thing, Sam," said Leonard.

I was flat flabbergasted by Pa, and so was Mr. Perkins. "Mailing May?" he mumbled, shaking his head.

"Let's see. The postal code says not to mail lizards or insects or anything smelly." Mr. Perkins looked at me over his glasses and then sniffed. "Guess you pass the smell test."

"But what about girls?" I asked. "Can you mail me?"

"Well, the rule book says nothing about children, but it is permissible to mail baby chicks." Mr. Perkins smiled. "Let's find out exactly how much you and your valise weigh."

I scrambled up onto the big scale, and Pa set his traveling bag next to me.

"Forty-eight pounds and eight ounces. Biggest baby chick on record!" Mr. Perkins ran his finger down a chart hanging near the scale and turned to Pa. "To mail May from Grangeville to Lewiston will cost fifty-three cents. Well, Leonard, looks like you'll be in charge of some poultry on this mail run."

Before I knew it, Mr. Perkins had glued fifty-three cents worth of stamps on the back of my coat, along with a label that read:

Mrs. C. G. Vennigerholz
1156 Twelfth Ave
Lewiston, Idaho

DELIVER TO

Pa hugged me and told me to be good for Grandma Mary. Then he was gone, and there I was, a package sitting in the post office. Before long, Leonard carted me and the rest of the mail to the train station. The big black steam engine was already waiting, hissing and snorting like a boar hog. The sight made me go all tingly, seeing as I'd never ever ridden on a train before.

After Leonard loaded the mailbags and a few other packages, he called out, "Time to go, May." Then he helped me up the steel steps.

At exactly seven o'clock, the train chugged away from my home and headed down the mountain. I felt as adventuresome as Daniel Boone!

The inside of the mail car was like a little post office, and Leonard got busy right away sorting mail to be dropped off at towns along the way. I curled up nearby the stove to keep warm and watched.

Whenever Leonard had a free minute, he'd take me to the door for a look. My, oh, my, what sights there were to see! Why, we hung on the edge of mountainsides and crawled through tunnels. We crossed deep valleys on top of tall, spidery trestles that Leonard called "steel on stilts."

Then long about Lapwai Canyon, where the train track twists back and forth down the mountain, I began to feel somewhat less adventuresome. Instead, I was feeling dizzy and weak in the stomach. I was about to run to get some fresh air when I heard an angry voice at the door.

"Leonard," yelled a man in a uniform, "that girl better have a ticket or money to buy one."

It was Mr. Harry Morris, the train's conductor. I hid behind Leonard as he explained that I was a package, not a passenger. Then he showed Mr. Morris the stamps on my coat. That cranky old conductor slapped his knee and laughed out loud.

"I've seen everything now," said Mr. Morris, wiping his eyes.

Well, Mr. Morris plumb scared the dizziness right out of me! Even my stomach seemed better, and I started feeling hungry. Leonard said lunch would be at Grandma Mary's.

The train made a few more stops at towns like Sweetwater and Joseph before we pulled into the Lewiston railroad station. Since this was the end of the line, Leonard had time to be my mail carrier, and we headed for Grandma Mary's place.

293

The second I laid eyes on Grandma Mary, I felt downright warm inside. Ma and Pa had kept their promise after all—with a little help from the U.S. Post Office!

MICHAEL O. TUNNELL

About the Author

When Michael O. Tunnell heard a teacher reading a story to a group of students, he knew he wanted to write children's books. Mr. Tunnell thought he would write fantasy stories, but most of his stories are about real events. "I'm just fascinated when it comes to history," he said. "It's important to show history is made up of stories of all of the rest of us, not just famous people."

Mr. Tunnell lives in Utah and teaches college students about children's literature. He and his wife, Glenna, have four children and one grandchild.

About the Illustrator

TED RAND

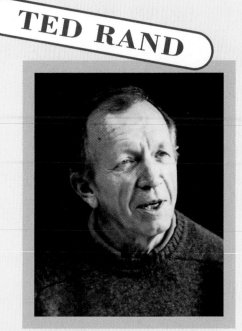

Ted Rand also illustrated the book *Knots on a Counting Rope* by Bill Martin, Jr., and John Archambault. Mr. Rand has lived in Washington state all his life, except for the four years he spent in the Navy.

Reader Response

Open for Discussion

Pretend that you can walk into the illustrations for *Mailing May*. As you stand in each picture, look around. What do you see, hear, smell, and feel?

Comprehension Check

1. May's feelings change during the story. Name three feelings that May has and tell why she feels each way.

2. The story takes place a long time ago, and the author helps us see this by using some old-fashioned expressions — words and phrases that we may know, but that we don't use much today. Make a list of old-fashioned expressions you see and tell what they mean.

3. The families in both *Mailing May* and *Leah's Pony* talk about hard times. Which family seems to be having the worse time? How can you tell?

4. The **setting** of *Mailing May* is 1914 in Idaho. What details in the story and pictures tell you that this story takes place a long time ago?

5. If the **setting** of the story were today, how would the story be different?

Oh, Grandma!

It is 1914. Pretend you are arriving at last at Grandma Mary's house. What will you tell her about your train ride? How will you act? Work with two partners and take turns being Leonard, Grandma Mary, and May to act out the scene.

Visualizing

- To **visualize** is to create a picture in your mind.

- You can put yourself into the story or article by using all your senses when you read.

- When you read, you may be able to use details in the text along with what you know about the subject to see, hear, smell, taste, and feel what the author describes.

Read "First Day in London" from *You Can't Eat Your Chicken Pox, Amber Brown* **by Paula Danziger.**

Talk About It

1. What two details help you visualize Aunt Pam?

2. What are you visualizing about Amber? What details from the story and what from your experience help you visualize her?

First Day in London

by Paula Danziger

"Elevators Ho," I yell as we enter the elevator.

There are mirrors in it.

Aunt Pam looks really good. She's wearing a flowered sundress and carrying a really pretty sweater.

Her long blond hair is in one long braid.

And she has makeup on and this really pretty-smelling perfume.

On her feet are walking shoes.

Aunt Pam is ready to show me London.

I look in the mirror.

I'm wearing a long purple shirt. The shirt is so long that it's hard to see the denim shorts under it.

I've got sandals on.

My hair is just hanging there.

It was too tired to get put into ponytails or anything.

I'm not sure that I am ready for London.

As we leave the building, I hear someone call out, "Pam, welcome back."

Aunt Pam turns and smiles. "Amber, I want to introduce you to Mary. She's the housekeeper here ... and over the years has become a friend."

"Welcome to London, Amber. Is this your first time in our city?"

I smile and nod. "It's Amber's first day and we're off to see Trafalgar Square," Aunt Pam tells Mary as she takes my hand and walks up to the curb to get a cab. Even though I'm too big to hold hands anymore, I hold her hand. "Amber, do you remember what I told you about cars in this country?"

I'm so tired ... and the cars are driving on the wrong side of the road, just like Aunt Pam told me.

LOOK AHEAD TO

The Extra-Good Sunday

In the next story, Ramona and Beezus have to cook Sunday dinner for the whole family. Read and visualize how they prepare the family meal.

Vocabulary

Words to Know

flushed   pronounced   sauce
hurled   refrigerator   success

Words with similar meanings are **synonyms.** You can figure out the meaning of an unknown word by looking for a clue around it. The clue might be a synonym.

Read the paragraph below. Notice how *threw* helps you understand what *hurled* means.

The Quick Cook!

Leah wanted to make a special ice-cream sauce for Grandma's party, but the party was in two hours! She took milk from the refrigerator. Then she hurled chocolate chips into a bowl—she just threw them in so she could be quick. "Finished—just in time," pronounced Leah. Her face was flushed and red from running around the kitchen, but the delicious sauce was a success.

Write About It

Write about the first time someone you know tried to cook something. Use several vocabulary words.

300

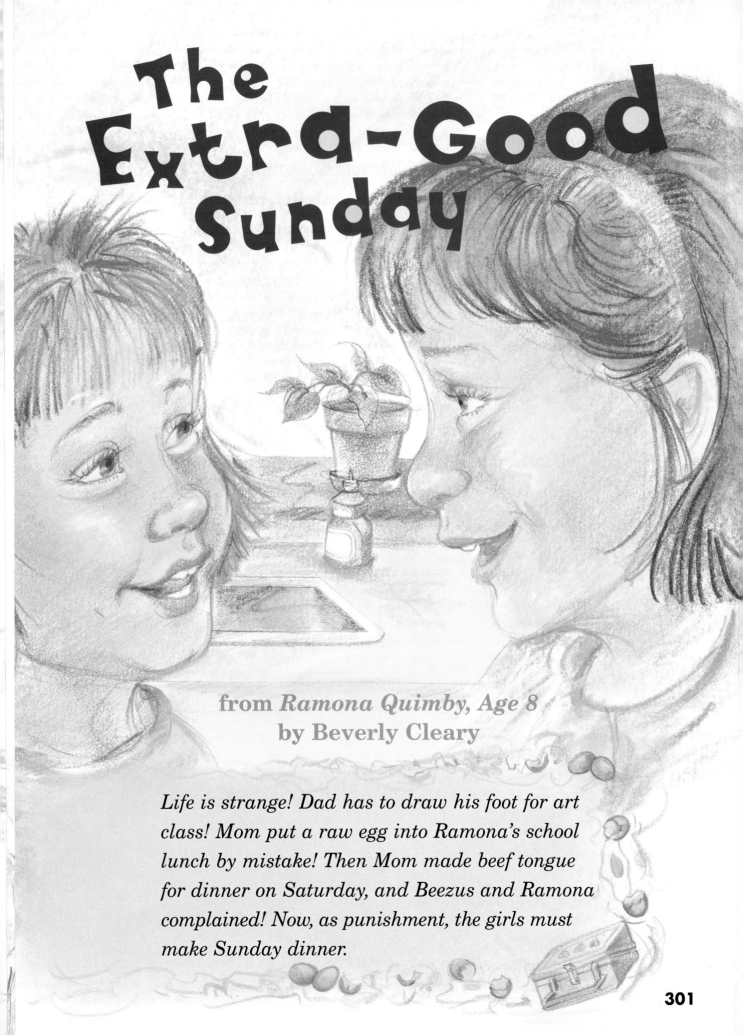

The Extra-Good Sunday

from *Ramona Quimby, Age 8*
by Beverly Cleary

Life is strange! Dad has to draw his foot for art class! Mom put a raw egg into Ramona's school lunch by mistake! Then Mom made beef tongue for dinner on Saturday, and Beezus and Ramona complained! Now, as punishment, the girls must make Sunday dinner.

Beezus opened the cupboard of canned goods. "But there isn't any mushroom soup," she said. "What are we going to do?"

"Mix up something wet," suggested Ramona. "It would serve them right if it tasted awful."

"Why don't we make something awful?" asked Beezus. "So they will know how we feel when we have to eat tongue."

"What tastes really awful?" Ramona was eager to go along with the suggestion, united with her sister against their enemy—for the moment, their parents.

Beezus, always practical, changed her mind. "It wouldn't work. We have to eat it too, and they're so mean we'll probably have to do the dishes besides. Anyway, I guess you might say our honor is at stake, because they think we can't cook a good meal."

Ramona was ready with another solution. "Throw everything in one dish."

Beezus opened the package of chicken thighs and stared at them with distaste. "I can't stand touching raw meat," she said, as she picked up a thigh between two forks.

"Do we have to eat the skin?" asked Ramona. "All those yucky little bumps."

Beezus found a pair of kitchen tongs. She tried holding down a thigh with a fork and pulling off the skin with the tongs.

"Here, let me hold it," said Ramona, who was not squeamish about touching such things as worms or raw meat. She took a firm hold on the thigh while Beezus grasped the skin with the tongs. Both pulled, and the skin peeled away. They played tug-of-war with each thigh, leaving a sad-looking heap of skins on the counter and a layer of chicken thighs in the glass dish.

"Can't you remember what little specks Mother uses?" asked Beezus. Ramona could not. The girls studied the spice shelf, unscrewed jar lids and sniffed. Nutmeg? No. Cloves? Terrible. Cinnamon?

Uh-uh. Chili powder? Well . . . Yes, that must be it. Ramona remembered that the specks were red. Beezus stirred half a teaspoon of the dark red powder into the yogurt, which she poured over the chicken. She slid the dish into the oven set at 350 degrees, the temperature for chicken recommended by the cookbook.

From the living room came the sound of their parents' conversation, sometimes serious and sometimes highlighted by laughter. While we're slaving out here, thought Ramona, as she climbed up on the counter to reach the box of cornmeal. After she climbed down, she discovered she had to climb up again for baking powder and soda. She finally knelt on the counter to save time and asked Beezus to bring her an egg.

"It's a good thing Mother can't see you up there," remarked Beezus, as she handed Ramona an egg.

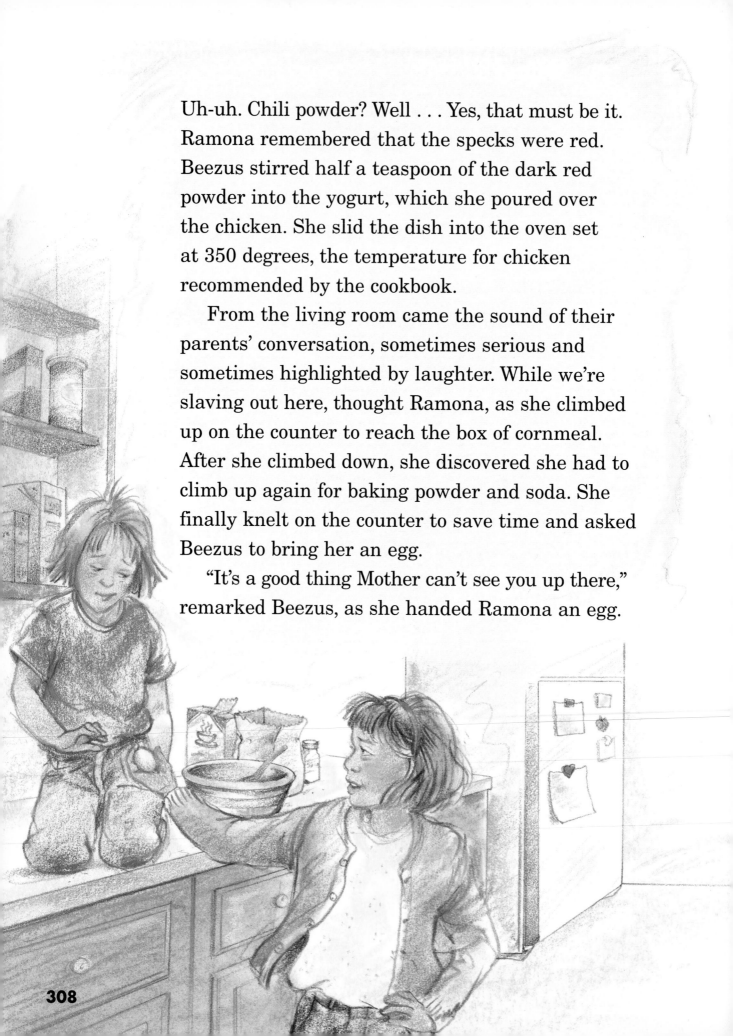

"How else am I supposed to reach things?" Ramona successfully broke the egg and tossed the shell onto the counter. "Now I need buttermilk."

Beezus broke the news. There was no buttermilk in the refrigerator. "What'll I do?" whispered Ramona in a panic.

"Here. Use this." Beezus thrust the carton of banana yogurt at her sister. "Yogurt is sort of sour, so it might work."

The kitchen door opened a crack. "What's going on in there?" inquired Mr. Quimby.

Beezus hurled herself against the door. "You stay out!" she ordered. "Dinner is going to be a—surprise!"

For a moment Ramona thought Beezus had been going to say a mess. She stirred egg and yogurt together, measured flour, spilling some on the floor, and then discovered she was short of cornmeal. More panic.

"My cooking teacher says you should always check to see if you have all the ingredients before you start to cook," said Beezus.

"Oh, be quiet." Ramona reached for a package of Cream of Wheat, because its grains were about the same size as cornmeal. She scattered only a little on the floor.

Something was needed to sop up the sauce with little red specks when the chicken was served. Rice! The spilled Cream of Wheat gritted underneath Beezus's feet as she measured rice and boiled water according to the directions on the package.

When the rice was cooking, she slipped into the dining room to set the table and then remembered they had forgotten salad. Salad! Carrot sticks were quickest. Beezus began to scrape carrots into the sink.

"Yipe!" yelped Ramona from the counter. "The rice!" The lid of the pan was chittering. Beezus snatched a larger pan from the cupboard and transferred the rice.

"Do you girls need any help?" Mrs. Quimby called from the living room.

"No!" answered her daughters.

Another calamity. The corn bread should bake at 400 degrees, a higher temperature than that needed for the chicken. What was Ramona to do?

"Stick it in the oven anyway." Beezus's face was flushed.

In went the corn bread beside the chicken.

"Dessert!" whispered Beezus. All she could find was a can of boring pear halves. Back to the cookbook. "Heat with a little butter and serve with jelly in each half," she read. Jelly. Half a jar of apricot jam would have to do. The pears and butter went into the saucepan. Never mind the syrup spilled on the floor.

"Beezus!" Ramona held up the package of peas.

Beezus groaned. Out came the partially cooked chicken while she stirred the thawing peas into the yogurt and shoved the dish back into the oven.

The rice! They had forgotten the rice, which was only beginning to stick to the pan. Quick! Take it off the burner. How did their mother manage to get everything cooked at the right time? Put the carrot sticks on a dish. Pour the milk. "Candles!" Beezus whispered. "Dinner might look better if we have candles."

Ramona found two candle holders and two partly melted candles of uneven length. One of them had been used in a Halloween jack-o'-lantern. Beezus struck the match to light them, because although Ramona was brave about touching raw meat, she was skittish about lighting matches.

Was the chicken done? The girls anxiously examined their main dish, bubbling and brown around the edges. Beezus stabbed a thigh with a fork, and when it did not bleed, she decided it must be done. A toothpick pricked into the corn bread came out clean. The corn bread was done—flat, but done.

Grit, grit, grit sounded under the girls' feet.
It was amazing how a tiny bit of spilled Cream of
Wheat could make the entire kitchen floor gritty.
At last their dinner was served, the dining-room
light turned off, dinner announced, and the cooks,
tense with anxiety that was hidden by candlelight,
fell into their chairs as their parents seated
themselves. Was this dinner going to be edible?

"Candles!" exclaimed Mrs. Quimby. "What a
festive meal!"

"Let's taste it before we decide," said Mr.
Quimby with his most wicked grin.

The girls watched anxiously as their father took his first bite of the chicken. He chewed thoughtfully and said with more surprise than necessary, "Why this is good!"

"It really is," agreed Mrs. Quimby, and took a bit of corn bread. "Very good, Ramona," she said.

Mr. Quimby tasted the corn bread. "Just like Grandmother used to make," he pronounced.

The girls exchanged suppressed smiles. They could not taste the banana yogurt, and by candlelight, no one could tell that the corn bread was a little pale. The chicken, Ramona decided, was not as good as her parents thought—or pretended to think—but she could eat it without gagging.

Everyone relaxed, and Mrs. Quimby said chili powder was more interesting than paprika and asked which recipe they had used for the chicken.

Ramona answered, "Our own," as she exchanged another look with Beezus. Paprika! Those little specks in the sauce should have been paprika.

"We wanted to be creative," said Beezus.

Conversation was more comfortable than it had been the previous evening. Mr. Quimby said he was finally satisfied with his drawing which looked like a real foot. Beezus said her cooking class was studying the food groups everyone should eat every day. Ramona said there was this boy at school who called her Egghead. Mr. Quimby explained that Egghead was slang for a very smart person.

Ramona began to feel better.

The meal was a success. If the chicken did not taste as good as the girls had hoped and the corn bread did not rise like their mother's, both were edible. Beezus and Ramona were silently grateful to their parents for enjoying—or pretending to enjoy—their cooking. The whole family cheered up. When they had finished their pears with apricot jam, Ramona gave her mother a shy smile.

Mrs. Quimby smiled back and patted Ramona's hand. Ramona felt much lighter. Without using words, she had forgiven her mother for the unfortunate egg, and her mother had understood. Ramona could be happy again.

"You cooks have worked so hard," said Mr. Quimby, "that I'm going to wash the dishes. I'll even finish clearing the table."

"I'll help," volunteered Mrs. Quimby.

The girls exchanged another secret smile as they excused themselves and skipped off to their rooms before their parents discovered the pile of chicken skins and the broken eggshell on the counter, the carrot scrapings in the sink, and the Cream of Wheat, flour, and pear syrup on the floor.

About the Author
Beverly Cleary

When Beverly Cleary was in the third grade, she had these questions about the books she read: Why don't people write books about the sort of boys and girls who live on my block? Why doesn't something happen on every page? Why aren't the stories funny?

Ms. Cleary decided that she would write books about ordinary boys and girls doing funny things. That way other children would have the kinds of books she always wanted to read.

Beverly Cleary has written dozens of books and received many awards for her books about Ramona, Henry Huggins, and other real-life, funny, wonderful characters.

Reader Response

Have you had a frantic but funny time over food as Beezus and Ramona do? Tell about it.

Comprehension Check

1. Are the Quimbys a happy family or an unhappy family? Support your answer with examples.

2. Do you think that Beezus and Ramona do a good job fixing dinner? Why or why not?

3. What do you think Mom and Dad will say and do when they see the messy kitchen? Why do you think so?

4. Use all of your senses to **visualize** the dinner table when the Quimby family sits down to eat. What details from the story help you?

5. Think about the mess in the kitchen. What senses can you use to **visualize** the scene? Describe the kitchen.

Story Theater

Work with two partners to find some good action scenes of Ramona and Beezus in the kitchen. Then as one partner reads the scene, the other two partners pantomime what the girls do. As a group, decide what kind of music would go with your scene.

Plot

- **Plot** includes the important events of a story that happen in the beginning, middle, and end, and how those events happen.

- Events that are important to the plot help keep the story going.

Read "A Moon Landing" from *Grandpa Takes Me to the Moon* by Timothy R. Gaffney.

Write About It

1. Look at the beginning of the story. Write two important events that happen in the beginning.

2. Write two important events that happen in the middle of the story. Share them with a classmate.

A Moon Landing

by Timothy R. Gaffney

A boy imagines himself landing on the moon with his grandfather, who had been an astronaut.

We touch down on a flat plain with round, gray mountains on the horizon. There are no colors, just shades of gray. The sun is shining, but the sky is black like night. There is no air on the moon to make the sky blue. Space and black sky come right down to the ground.

We put on our space helmets. We have to back out the little door on our hands and knees. We climb down the ladder and step onto the moon.

Our spacesuits are thick and heavy, but everything weighs much less on the moon. Grandpa bounces when he walks. I pick up a rock and let it drop. It falls in slow motion to the ground.

Dust splashes up around it and falls back like water.

We unload the buggy. Grandpa calls it the lunar rover. We drive away on it until the moon lander looks like a little toy.

We stop several times to scoop up soil and rocks to take back to Earth. Pieces of the moon. We scoop them up and put them in bags, just like that.

High overhead is the Earth. It reminds me of the moon when it's almost full, but its bright side is colored blue and white by oceans and clouds.

"Time to go home," Grandpa says.

Before we leave, we plant an American flag on the moon. A small arm on the flagpole holds the flag out like it's waving in a breeze. We step back and salute it. Then we climb back into the moon lander and blast off.

We return to the capsule and it takes us back to earth. Splash! We're home.

LOOK AHEAD TO

Floating Home

In the next story, a girl decides to draw her house from space. Read and discover how the plot's important events happen as she makes her way into space.

Vocabulary

Words to Know

astronaut launch weighed
emergency unusual globe

Words with opposite meanings are **antonyms.** You can often figure out the meaning of an unknown word by finding a clue nearby. Sometimes this clue is an antonym.

Read the paragraph below. Notice how *ordinary* helps you understand the meaning of *unusual*.

A Letter Home from Space Camp

Being here has been so unusual—not like an ordinary summer at home! We learned how an astronaut circles the globe in a spaceship. We saw a film of a shuttle launch and learned how pilots make emergency landings if things go wrong. Our group went on a "moon mission." I weighed a lot less on the moon than on Earth! I'll tell you more when I'm home.

Write About It

Write a headline about the latest mission in space—real or imaginary. Use some vocabulary words.

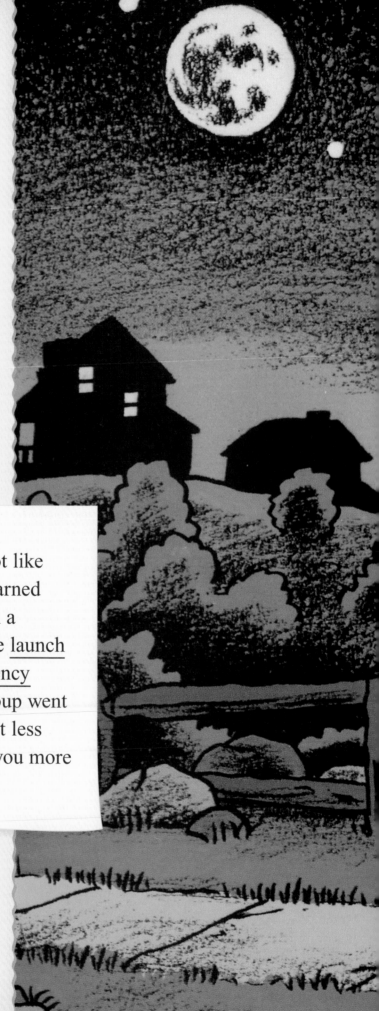

Floating Home

written by David Getz
illustrated by Michael Rex

When Mrs. Selinsky asked the class to look at their homes in a new way and to draw what they saw, Maxine left school and kept on walking.

She passed Kevin outside his house, sitting on the branch of a tree, studying his home as if he were a squirrel.

She passed Selina lying in the grass in her front yard, looking up at her apartment building as if she were an ant.

She passed Oscar in dark sunglasses, standing in front of his home, pretending he was a stranger.

Artist's pad under her arm, her unsharpened colored pencils in their box, and a globe sharpener with all the countries of the world in her overalls pocket, Maxine passed her own home and kept on walking.

**Kennedy Space Center
at Cape Canaveral in Florida**

She was going to draw the most unusual picture
of all, a picture of the Earth from space. She was
going to be the youngest astronaut of all time!

Maxine checked into her room, wrote a letter to
her mom and dad, and undressed to take a shower.

She knew it would be the last shower she would
take for two weeks.

You don't shower in the space shuttle. Water does
not fall from the nozzle.

Nothing falls inside a shuttle in space. Water
spraying out of a shower would float all over the place
and quickly fill the cabin with dancing beads of liquid.

Maxine turned on the hot water. She let herself
disappear in a cloud of steam.

She washed her hair.

She opened a window to let the steam escape.

Her last breakfast on Earth was in three hours.

Her crewmates ate very little.

Maxine had a cup of orange juice and a bowl
of cereal.

She was disappointed there was no prize in her cereal box. She watched the milk pour from the container. Down it flowed. Down.

Soon there would be no down in the shuttle. Down is where things fall.

In space, nothing falls.

She couldn't pour milk in space.

Suddenly newspaper and television reporters burst into the room.

"Maxine!" one of them called out. "Are you afraid?"

"Maxine," another asked, "how does it feel to be the first eight-year-old astronaut?"

"Maxine, are you going to miss your parents?"

"Maxine, why are you doing it?"

"Art," Maxine told them. "I'm doing it for art."

"Time to get dressed!" said a NASA official.

More reporters were waiting for her in the suit room. They were there to watch her get dressed.

She was glad this didn't happen at home every morning.

The pressure suit was meant to protect her should anything happen to the shuttle before it rose to nineteen miles above the ground. The suit was big and orange, and she didn't put it on as much as climb into it. Through a slit in the back Maxine shoved one leg, then the other, and then her arms. She poked her head through the tight neck band at the top of the suit. The boots locked onto the pants cuffs. The gloves locked onto the sleeves, and the helmet locked onto the collar.

The people from NASA put all sorts of things in her pockets: special gloves to keep her warm if she needed to parachute out of the shuttle and land in the ocean; an emergency radio; survival gear; sharpener and colored pencils. They also gave her a small mirror.

"Place it on your lap," someone said. "You'll be able to see out the window above your head."

It was time to go out to the pad.

Feeling like a hundred-pound duck, Maxine waddled over to the van that would take her to the launch pad.

It was 3 A.M. and dark outside. Maxine had never been outside at 3 A.M. before.

"So this is what the world looks like when I'm sleeping," she said to herself.

And then she saw the shuttle. It was alive.

Suspended above the pad, the vehicle was lit by dazzlingly bright xenon lights as if it were an actor, stage center, ready for his big speech.

And it was breathing. Exhaling steam from its top and bottom, it reminded Maxine of a dragon.

The orbiter itself looked like a stubby airplane. It rode piggyback on a huge orange fuel tank as tall as a fifteen-story building. Filled with liquid hydrogen and oxygen, the orange tank would supply the fuel for the shuttle's main engines.

On either side of the orange tank were the two solid rocket boosters. Loaded with chunks of solid fuel like skyscrapers stuffed with gunpowder, these boosters would help lift the shuttle off the pad and into space.

Maxine entered the shuttle's orbiter through a porthole. Since the shuttle was pointed straight up, ready for launch, the back wall was actually her floor. To protect the panels and instruments from the astronauts' heavy feet, the wall was covered with a thick pad.

"Some art project," a technician said, and helped strap Maxine into her seat.

"I hope your mom puts your drawing on her refrigerator," another technician said, and checked her suit. He made sure it was in working order.

The technicians removed the padding covering the back wall and, one by one, stepped out through the porthole.

As the door closed, Maxine checked to make sure her pad, pencils, and sharpener were still there.

The countdown began.

With two minutes to go, the controllers at Cape Canaveral announced over the radio, "Close and lock your visors. Turn on your suit oxygen. Have a nice flight."

Maxine placed the mirror on her lap. She could see through the window above her head. She saw nothing but clouds and a clear blue sky.

Then she did as she was told. She lowered her visor and began to breathe oxygen from her suit.

The main engines started. Everything began to tremble. It was a familiar feeling, like being in a subway train. The vibrations jostled her mirror.

Then the whole shuttle began to sway.

Suddenly the rumbling became thunderous; the gentle subway became an earthquake. Everything shuddered and shook.

The shuttle swayed back. The solid rockets ignited.

The noise!

Like a thousand thousand lions roaring! Like the heart of an immense raging fire. *Roar!*

Boom!

She was pressed deep into her seat.

Then something kicked her in the back.

Then . . . up!

"We are going!" she told herself. "We are definitely going somewhere!"

Up! Up!

Launch!

Looking into her mirror, she could see the launch pad dropping away at a dizzying speed. Rapidly everything on the ground became smaller and smaller.

Up! Up!

One . . . two . . . three . . . four . . . five . . . six . . . seven . . . flying faster and faster . . . eight! The shuttle began to roll.

Over, then over.

Maxine watched the sunlight fly across the cabin.

She was flying upside down.

Invisible hands pushed her deep into her seat.

The shuttle hurtled through the thick atmosphere.

The wind howled.

In twenty seconds, she was traveling faster than the speed of sound, faster than the word *hello* travels from one person's mouth to another's ear— 760 miles per hour! One mile every five seconds!

Faster, then faster. The shuttle tore through the thick atmosphere.

At two minutes, their fuel completely used up, the solid rocket boosters were no longer necessary. It was time to get rid of them.

Bang! The separation motors jettisoned the solid rocket boosters away from the shuttle. It felt like a giant had whacked the shuttle with a big stick.

The cabin lit up. For a frightening second everything was fire and smoke outside the windows.

Then clear.

Then quiet.

Maxine imagined the empty rocket canisters under their parachutes, drifting back down to Earth. They would be picked up in the ocean.

Now the ride was glass smooth. And impossibly fast.

Within eight minutes of launch, Maxine was traveling 11,000 miles per hour, or almost 190 miles a minute. Three miles a second.

The acceleration continued to press her deep into her seat, made her face feel as if a heavy weight were pushing against it, made her chest feel as if a gorilla were sitting on her ribs.

It was hard to breathe. She took quick, shallow, sharp breaths.

She couldn't move, couldn't lift her arms.

Then the three main engines cut off.

Suddenly everything was funny. In less than a heartbeat, Maxine went from feeling as if she weighed two hundred pounds to feeling as if she weighed nothing at all.

She was in space.

Her eyes seemed to float in her head. Her stomach floated in her belly. She floated within her suit.

She felt giddy . . . and a little sick.

"We made it!"

Someone laughed.

All around the cabin, things were floating. Checklists attached to panels by strings drifted like sea plants. Her mirror gently tumbled over and over through the air of the cabin.

335

"Maxine," someone called to her, "look up!" There in the window was Earth.

It was dazzling, sitting like a royal-blue gem on black velvet.

At its curved edge, on the horizon, was a thin, bright, fluorescent-blue band. The atmosphere.

She was looking down at the air she had breathed.

Somewhere down there her house sat at the bottom of the atmosphere. Her parents were breathing its air.

Suddenly something drew a long, thin streak beneath her.

It was a shooting star. A chunk of rock from space had sliced through the atmosphere and burned up.

She was looking down at the shooting stars.

The shuttle passed over a funnel of clouds, a hurricane. Where the sky was clear, she could see shades of brown, gray, green. All that blue.

But where was her home? Where was her town, her city? Her state? She removed her globe sharpener, with all the countries.

She looked out the window. Somebody had forgotten to draw in the lines! Where were the lines that divided up the continents into countries? Where were the lines that divided up the countries into states, the states into cities?

There were no lines. It was just one Earth.

It was her home.

About the Author
David Getz

Is *Floating Home* a science book or isn't it?
In this story, David Getz combines fiction
and nonfiction to create a story about a
girl who goes into space. Mr. Getz wrote
the book *Floating Home* after interviewing
astronauts and officials from the National
Aeronautics and Space Administration
(NASA).

Mr. Getz is an elementary school science
teacher in New York City. He and his wife
have one daughter, Maxine.

About the Illustrator
Michael Rex

Michael Rex says that "being an astronaut
is the only profession I'd give up drawing
for." *Floating Home* is the first book that Mr.
Rex illustrated. Since then, he has illustrated
other books, including *The Painting Gorilla,*
which he also wrote. Michael Rex lives in
New York.

Reader Response

Open for Discussion

If you had a chance to go on the space shuttle with Maxine, would you go? What would your home look like from space?

Comprehension Check

1. What did Mrs. Selinsky mean when she told students to look at their homes in a new way? Do you think she expected students to do what Maxine did?

2. What kind of person is Maxine? What parts of the story support your ideas?

3. Could this story really happen? Why or why not?

4. List three main **plot** events in *Floating Home*.

5. Is Maxine's writing a letter home an important **plot** event?

Home Sweet Home

Maxine's assignment was to look at her home in a new way and sketch what she saw. In addition to space travel, what are some other ways to look at your home in a new way? Choose one of those ways and create a picture of your home.

Skill Lesson

Realism and Fantasy

- A **realistic story** tells about something that could happen in real life.

- A **fantasy** has some things that could not possibly happen. Some also have things that could happen.

Read "Ali and the Snake" from _The Girl Who Wore Snakes_ by Angela Johnson and "Verdi Wonders" from _Verdi_ by Janell Cannon.

Write About It

1. Write _Snakes_ at the top of a piece of paper. Write _realistic_ at the top left and _fantasy_ at the top right. Write details from each story under the correct word.

2. Decide which story is realistic and which one is a fantasy. Tell why you think as you do.

The Girl Who Wore Snakes
story by Angela Johnson · paintings by James E. Ransome

Ali and the Snake
by Angela Johnson

When the man from the zoo came to Ali's school, he brought Silvia, the snake.

She was brown, yellow, and orange, and made Ali think of the sun and the earth and everything in between.

The zoo man said, "Who wants to hold her?"

Ali said, "Me"—and wore Silvia, the brown, yellow, and orange snake, all day long around her neck, around her arms, and around her ankles.

After Silvia went back to the zoo, Ali became known as "the girl who wore the snake."

Verdi Wonders

by Janell Cannon

On a small tropical island, the sun rose high above the steamy jungle. A mother python was sending her hatchlings out into the forest the way all mother pythons do. "Grow up big and green—as green as the trees' leaves," she called to her little yellow babies as they happily scattered among the trees.

But Verdi dawdled. He was proudly eyeing his bright yellow skin. He especially liked the bold stripes that zigzagged down his back. Why the hurry to grow up big and green? he wondered.

Maybe some of the older snakes in the jungle could tell him. Verdi ventured into the treetops to look for them.

Two Bad Ants

In the next story, two ants decide not to return home with the other ants. Read and decide for yourself if ants could really have such a fantastic adventure.

341

Words to Know

blinding	crystal	echoing
treasure	ledge	sparkling
scout	remarkable	

When you read, you may come across a word you don't know. To figure out its meaning, look for clues in the other sentences. A clue might be found in an explanation or definition given near the word.

What do you think *ledge* means? Find an explanation or definition in a sentence near it.

A Dangerous Adventure

The scout slowly crept along the canyon's ledge. The rocky shelf was narrow and steep. He gripped the crystal as blinding sunlight shone off the sparkling stone. This remarkable treasure would make him famous. Suddenly he slipped and sent rocks tumbling over the side. The sound of falling rock echoing off the walls reminded him to be more careful.

Talk About It

What happens next? Use vocabulary words to tell how the story ends.

TWO BAD ANTS

written and illustrated by Chris Van Allsburg

The news traveled swiftly through the tunnels of the ant world. A scout had returned with a remarkable discovery—a beautiful sparkling crystal. When the scout presented the crystal to the ant queen she took a small bite, then quickly ate the entire thing.

She deemed it the most delicious food she had ever tasted. Nothing could make her happier than to have more, much more. The ants understood. They were eager to gather more crystals because the queen was the mother of them all. Her happiness made the whole ant nest a happy place.

It was late in the day when they departed. Long shadows stretched over the entrance to the ant kingdom. One by one the insects climbed out, following the scout, who had made it clear—there were many crystals where the first had been found, but the journey was long and dangerous.

They marched into the woods that surrounded their underground home. Dusk turned to twilight, twilight to night. The path they followed twisted and turned, every bend leading them deeper into the dark forest.

More than once the line of ants stopped
and anxiously listened for the sounds of
hungry spiders. But all they heard was the call
of the crickets echoing through the woods like
distant thunder.

Dew formed on the leaves above. Without
warning, huge cold drops fell on the marching
ants. A firefly passed overhead that, for an
instant, lit up the woods with a blinding flash
of blue-green light.

At the edge of the forest stood a mountain. The ants looked up and could not see its peak. It seemed to reach right to the heavens. But they did not stop. Up the side they climbed, higher and higher.

The wind whistled through the cracks of the mountain's face. The ants could feel its force bending their delicate antennae. Their legs grew weak as they struggled upward. At last they reached a ledge and crawled through a narrow tunnel.

When the ants came out of the tunnel they found themselves in a strange world. Smells they had known all their lives, smells of dirt and grass and rotting plants, had vanished. There was no more wind and, most puzzling of all, it seemed that the sky was gone.

They crossed smooth shiny surfaces, then followed the scout up a glassy, curved wall. They had reached their goal. From the top of the wall they looked below to a sea of crystals. One by one the ants climbed down into the sparkling treasure.

Quickly they each chose a crystal, then turned to start the journey home. There was something about this unnatural place that made the ants nervous. In fact they left in such a hurry that none of them noticed the two small ants who stayed behind.

"Why go back?" one asked the other. "This place may not feel like home, but look at all these crystals."

"You're right," said the other, "we can stay here and eat this tasty treasure every day, forever."

So the two ants ate crystal after crystal until they were too full to move, and fell asleep.

Daylight came. The sleeping ants were unaware of changes taking place in their new found home. A giant silver scoop hovered above them, then plunged deep into the crystals. It shoveled up both ants and crystals and carried them high into the air.

The ants were wide awake when the scoop turned, dropping them from a frightening height. They tumbled through space in a shower of crystals and fell into a boiling brown lake.

Then the giant scoop stirred violently back and forth. Crushing waves fell over the ants. They paddled hard to keep their tiny heads above water. But the scoop kept spinning the hot brown liquid.

Around and around it went, creating a whirlpool that sucked the ants deeper and deeper. They both held their breath and finally bobbed to the surface, gasping for air and spitting mouthfuls of the terrible, bitter water.

Then the lake tilted and began to empty into a cave. The ants could hear the rushing water and felt themselves pulled toward the pitch black hole.

Suddenly the cave disappeared and the lake became calm. The ants swam to the shore and found that the lake had steep sides.

They hurried down the walls that held back the lake. The frightened insects looked for a place to hide, worried that the giant scoop might shovel them up again. Close by they found a huge round disk with holes that could neatly hide them.

But as soon as they had climbed inside, their hiding place was lifted, tilted, and lowered into a dark space. When the ants climbed out of the holes they were surrounded by a strange red glow. It seemed to them that every second the temperature was rising.

It soon became so unbearably hot that they thought they would soon be cooked. But suddenly the disk they were standing on rocketed upward and the two hot ants went flying through the air.

They landed near what seemed to be a fountain—a waterfall pouring from a silver tube. Both ants had a powerful thirst and longed to dip their feverish heads into the refreshing water. They quickly climbed along the tube.

As they got closer to the rushing water the ants felt a cool spray. They tightly gripped the shiny surface of the fountain and slowly leaned their heads into the falling stream. But the force of the water was much too strong.

The tiny insects were pulled off the fountain and plunged down into a wet, dark chamber. They landed on half-eaten fruit and other soggy things. Suddenly the air was filled with loud, frightening sounds. The chamber began to spin.

The ants were caught in a whirling storm of shredded food and stinging rain. Then, just as quickly as it had started, the noise and spinning stopped. Bruised and dizzy, the ants climbed out of the chamber.

In daylight once again, they raced through puddles and up a smooth metal wall. In the distance they saw something comforting—two long, narrow holes that reminded them of the warmth and safety of their old underground home. They climbed up into the dark openings.

But there was no safety inside these holes. A strange force passed through the wet ants. They were stunned senseless and blown out of the holes like bullets from a gun. When they landed the tiny insects were too exhausted to go on. They crawled into a dark corner and fell fast asleep.

Night had returned when the battered ants awoke to a familiar sound—the footsteps of their fellow insects returning for more crystals. The two ants slipped quietly to the end of the line. They climbed the glassy wall and once again stood amid the treasure. But this time they each chose a single crystal and followed their friends home.

Standing at the edge of their ant hole, the two ants listened to the joyful sounds that came from below. They knew how grateful their mother queen would be when they gave her their crystals. At that moment, the two ants felt happier than they'd ever felt before. This was their home, this was their family. This was where they were meant to be.

About the Author/Illustrator
CHRIS VAN ALLSBURG

Chris Van Allsburg has been asked many times where his ideas come from. "The fact is," he says, "I don't know where my ideas come from. . . . It almost seems like a discovery, as if the story was always there. The few elements I start out with are actually clues. If I figure out what they mean, I can discover the story that's waiting."

When he creates a book, Mr. Van Allsburg usually begins by writing the story. He then makes rough sketches to decide from what angle each picture will be seen. When that is decided, he can experiment with light and shadows in his illustrations.

Mr. Van Allsburg likes to take walks and go to museums. He and his wife live in Rhode Island.

Reader Response

Open for Discussion

You are one of the bad ants. What will you tell your friends when you see them? Will you ever want to go exploring again? Why or why not?

Comprehension Check

1. Why do the two ants stay behind when the other ants take crystals to the queen?

2. What word besides *bad* describes the ants? Use your word to write a new title. Support your title with examples from the story.

3. The ants have no experience in kitchens, but you do. What ordinary kitchen items become dangers to the ants?

4. *Two Bad Ants* is a **fantasy** because some things that happen in the story could not really happen. Name something from the story that could not really happen.

5. Some things in a **fantasy** are real. Name two things from the story that could happen.

Classroom Trek

Work with a partner pretending to be two ants crossing your classroom. What would happen to you? What classroom items would you see, and what would you think they were? Act out your journey describing what you see and giving your partner safety tips.

PANDORA'S BOX

retold and illustrated by
Anne Rockwell

Reading Across Texts

Reading a Myth

✓ **Read the title.** It often tells who the main characters are. A myth has few characters and a simple plot.

✓ **Look for an explanation.** A myth is an old story that often explains how something in nature came to be. Myths are used to explain something that people long ago had a hard time understanding.

Focus Your Reading

This myth explains how trouble came into the world. As you read, think about the two bad ants and how their curiosity got them into trouble.

Pandora was made, not born as other people are. Hephaestus modeled her out of clay. He made her a young woman as beautiful as his wife, Aphrodite, the goddess of love and beauty.

Each of the gods and goddesses gave Pandora a gift. Then Athene, the goddess of wisdom, breathed life into her. Most of the gifts the gods gave her were good ones. But unfortunately Hermes, as always full of tricks and mischief, gave her more curiosity than was good for her.

Pandora was sent to live on Earth. She had no trouble finding a good husband, for the gods and goddesses had given her the gifts of smiles and sweetness and wit and winning ways. Besides that, she was rich, for as a wedding gift the gods and goddesses gave her a box that had been made by Hephaestus. It was as beautiful as Pandora and very valuable too.

"Never, never open that box!" all the gods and goddesses warned Pandora. She promised to obey them, but as time went on Pandora grew more and more curious about what was in the box that she had promised never to open.

In those days, there was no sadness among the mortals on Earth. And why should it have been otherwise? There was no sickness, no hunger, no jealousy, no laziness, no greed, no anger, no cruelty. Even death was like a long and gentle sleep when people were very tired. There was no suffering of any kind.

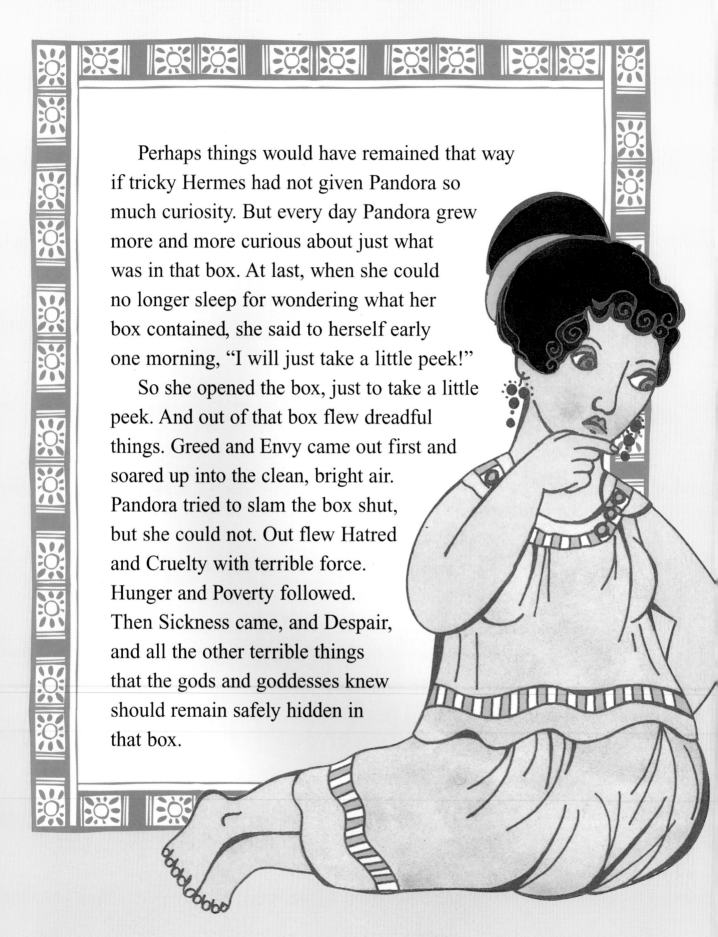

Perhaps things would have remained that way if tricky Hermes had not given Pandora so much curiosity. But every day Pandora grew more and more curious about just what was in that box. At last, when she could no longer sleep for wondering what her box contained, she said to herself early one morning, "I will just take a little peek!"

So she opened the box, just to take a little peek. And out of that box flew dreadful things. Greed and Envy came out first and soared up into the clean, bright air. Pandora tried to slam the box shut, but she could not. Out flew Hatred and Cruelty with terrible force. Hunger and Poverty followed. Then Sickness came, and Despair, and all the other terrible things that the gods and goddesses knew should remain safely hidden in that box.

Pandora had set them all free.

"Come back! Come back where you belong!" Pandora called out to the terrible things as they flew around her. She grabbed at them in the air, but they soared out of her reach and up into the sky. None came back. They are still out there bringing misery and trouble to people on Earth.

But the gods and goddesses had not put only dreadful things in Pandora's box. Hidden in among the terrible things was something small and fragile-winged and good. This thing was Hope. Who was the kindly god or goddess who thought to put Hope in among all the miseries and misfortunes? No one knows.

But because Hope was hidden in Pandora's box, whenever there is too much trouble and sadness among us mortals, Hope makes us think that tomorrow will be better.

And soon Pandora dried her tears.

"I hope I will never be too curious again!" she said.

And she never was.

The Limerick's Lively to Write

by David McCord

The limerick's lively to write:
Five lines to it—all nice and tight.
    Two long ones, two trick
    Little short ones, then quick
As a flash here's the last one in sight.

There Was an Old Man with a Flute

by Edward Lear

There was an Old Man with a flute.
A serpent ran into his boot;
    But he played day and night
    'Til the serpent took flight,
And avoided that man with a flute.

I Love the Look of Words

by Maya Angelou

Popcorn leaps, popping from the floor
of a hot black skillet
and into my mouth.
Black words leap,
snapping from the white
page. Rushing into my eyes. Sliding
into my brain which gobbles them
the way my tongue and teeth
chomp the buttered popcorn.

When I have stopped reading,
ideas from the words stay stuck
in my mind, like the sweet
smell of butter perfuming my
fingers long after the popcorn
is finished.

I love the book and the look of words
the weight of ideas that popped into my mind
I love the tracks
of new thinking in my mind.

Hugs and Kisses

by Charlotte Pomerantz

Mami, how long will you be away?

I'll be gone for a month, María.

Then give me a kiss for every day,
For every day that you are away.

That's thirty small kisses, María.
Treinta besitos, one for each day.
One for each day that I am away.
Treinta besitos, María.

Now give me a hug for every day,
For every day that you are away.

That's thirty big hugs, María.
Treinta abrazos, one for each day.
One for each day that I am away.
Treinta abrazos, María.

Now give me a doll for every day,
For every day that you are away.

That's thirty dollies, María.
Treinta muñecas, one for each day.
One for each day that I am away.
No, indeed, María.

Mail Myself to You

song lyrics by Woody Guthrie

I'm agonna wrap myself in paper;
I'm gonna daub myself with glue,
Stick some stamps on top of my head,
I'm gonna mail myself to you.

I'm agonna tie me up in a red string;
I'm gonna tie blue ribbons too.
I'm agonna climb in my mailbox;
I'm gonna mail myself to you.

When you see me in your mailbox,
Cut the string and let me out.
Wash the glue off my fingers;
Stick some bubble gum in my mouth.

Take me out of my wrapping paper;
Wash the stamps off my head.
Pour me full of ice cream sodies;
Put me in my nice warm bed.

Glossary

How to Use This Glossary

This glossary can help you understand and pronounce some of the words in this book. The entries in this glossary are in alphabetical order. There are guide words at the top of each page to show you the first and last words on the page. A pronunciation key is at the bottom of every other page. Remember, if you can't find the word you are looking for, ask for help or check a dictionary.

The entry word is in dark type. It shows how the word is spelled and how the word is divided into syllables.

The pronunciation is in parentheses. It also shows which syllables are stressed.

Part-of-speech labels show the function or functions of an entry word and any listed form of that word.

ar·rive (ə rīv′), VERB. to come to a place: *We arrived in Boston a week ago.* ❑ VERB **ar·rives, ar·rived, ar·riv·ing.**

Sometimes, irregular and other forms will be shown to help you use the word correctly.

The definition and example sentence show you what the word means and how it is used.

A a

al·pha·bet (al′fə bet), NOUN. the letters of a language arranged in a fixed order, not as they are in words. The English alphabet is: a b c d e f g h i j k l m n o p q r s t u v w x y z.

ap·pre·ci·ate (ə prē′shē āt), VERB. to be thankful for: *We appreciate your help in making the posters.* ❑ VERB **ap·pre·ci·ates, ap·pre·ci·at·ed, ap·pre·ci·at·ing.**

ar·rive (ə rīv′), VERB. to come to a place: *We arrived in Boston a week ago.* ❑ VERB **ar·rives, ar·rived, ar·riv·ing.**

as·ton·ish (ə ston′ish), VERB. to surprise greatly; amaze: *We were astonished at the force of the wind during the storm.* ❑ VERB **as·ton·ish·es, as·ton·ished, as·ton·ish·ing.**

as·tro·naut (as′trə nȯt), NOUN. a member of the crew of a spacecraft.

At·lan·tic (at lan′tik), NOUN. **Atlantic Ocean,** the ocean east of North and South America. It extends to Europe and Africa.

av•e•nue (av′ə nü), NOUN. a street, usually wide or bordered with trees. ❏ PLURAL **av•e•nues.**

B b

blind•ing (blīn′ding), ADJECTIVE. terribly bright; making someone unable to see: *Suddenly a blinding light lit the darkened room.*

bril•liant (bril′yənt), ADJECTIVE.
1 shining brightly; sparkling: *brilliant jewels, brilliant sunshine.*
2 having great ability or intelligence: *She is a brilliant mathematician.*

bun•dle (bun′dl),
1 NOUN. a number of things tied or wrapped together.
2 VERB. to tie or wrap together; make into a bundle: *We bundled all our old newspapers for the school's paper drive.* ❏ VERB **bun•dles, bun•dled, bun•dling.**

C c

cab•in (kab′ən), NOUN. a small, roughly built house; hut: *We spent the summer in a small log cabin in the woods.*

cart (kärt), VERB. to carry in or as if in a cart: *They came and carted the trash away.* ❏ VERB **carts, cart•ed, cart•ing.**

chore (chôr), NOUN. a small task or job that you have to do regularly: *Feeding our pets and washing the dishes are my daily chores.*

col•o•ny (kol′ə nē), NOUN. a group of people who leave their own country and go to settle in another land, but who still remain citizens of their own country: *The United States of America began as thirteen colonies.* ❏ PLURAL **col•o•nies.**

com•pass (kum′pəs), NOUN. a device for showing directions, with a magnetic needle that always points to the north: *The hikers used compasses to guide their way.* ❏ PLURAL **com•pass•es.**

compass

a hat	ė term	ô order	ch child	⎧a in about
ā age	i it	oi oil	ng long	⎪e in taken
ä far	ī ice	ou out	sh she	ə⎨i in pencil
â care	o hot	u cup	th thin	⎪o in lemon
e let	ō open	ù put	ŦH then	⎩u in circus
ē equal	ò saw	ü rule	zh measure	

con·den·sa·tion (kon′den sā′shən), NOUN. the process of changing from a gas or a vapor to a liquid.

con·duc·tor (kən duk′tər), NOUN.
1 someone in charge of a train and its passengers. The conductor often collects tickets or fares.
2 something that transmits heat, electricity, light, or sound: *Copper wire is used as a conductor of electricity.*

cone (kōn), NOUN.
1 a solid object with a flat, round base that narrows to a point at the top.
2 a scaly growth that bears the seeds on many evergreen trees.

con·quer (kong′kər), VERB. to win in war; get by fighting: *The evil knights conquered the defenseless kingdom.*
❏ VERB **con·quers, con·quered, con·quer·ing.**

cre·ate (krē āt′), VERB. to make something which has not been made before: *I am creating a new recipe for Mom's birthday dinner.*
❏ VERB **cre·ates, cre·at·ed, cre·at·ing.**

cru·el (krü′əl), ADJECTIVE. ready to hurt others or to enjoy their suffering: *The cruel man kicked his dog.*

crys·tal (kris′tl), NOUN. a hard, solid piece of some substance that is naturally formed of flat surfaces and angles. Crystals can be small, like grains of salt, or large, like some kinds of stone.

crystals

D d

de·light (di līt′), VERB. to please greatly: *The circus delighted us.*
❏ VERB **de·lights, de·light·ed, de·light·ing.**

de·sign (di zīn′), VERB. to make a first sketch of; plan out; arrange the form and color of: *My mother designed my coat and my grandmother made it.* ❑ VERB **de·signs, de·signed, de·sign·ing. –de·sign′er,** NOUN.

dis·tance (dis′təns), NOUN. a place far away: *She saw a light in the distance.*

dou·ble (dub′əl), ADJECTIVE. twice as much, as large, or as strong: *They were given double pay for working on a holiday.*

drag·on (drag′ən), NOUN. (in stories) a huge, fierce animal supposed to look like a winged lizard with scales and claws, and often supposed to breathe out fire and smoke.

duck·ling (duk′ling), NOUN. a young duck: *The ducklings followed their mother to the pond.*

dust (dust), NOUN. fine, dry, powdery earth: *Dust lay thick on the road.*

dragon

a	hat	ė	term	ô	order	ch	child	⎧a in about
ā	age	i	it	oi	oil	ng	long	⎪e in taken
ä	far	ī	ice	ou	out	sh	she	ə ⎨i in pencil
â	care	o	hot	u	cup	th	thin	⎪o in lemon
e	let	ō	open	ù	put	ŦH	then	⎩u in circus
ē	equal	ò	saw	ü	rule	zh	measure	

Ee

ech•o (ek′ō), VERB. to be heard again: *The sound was echoing through the valley.* ❏ VERB **ech•oes, ech•oed, ech•o•ing.**

e•mer•gen•cy (i mėr′jən sē), NOUN. a situation that calls for immediate action: *I keep tools in my car for use in an emergency.* ❏ PLURAL **e•mer•gen•cies.**

en•gine (en′jən), NOUN. a machine that changes energy from fuel, steam, water pressure, and so on, into motion and power. An engine is used to apply power to some work, such as running other machines.

e•vap•o•ra•tion (i vap′ə rā′shən), NOUN. the process of turning into a gas or vapor. Water returns to the atmosphere through evaporation.

ex•cite•ment (ek sīt′mənt), NOUN. an excited condition: *The birth of the new baby caused great excitement in the family.*

ex•plor•er (ek splôr′ər), NOUN. someone who travels into unknown areas in order to discover new things: *Astronauts are explorers of outer space.*

Ff

fa•mous (fā′məs), ADJECTIVE. very well known; noted: *The famous singer was greeted by a large crowd.*

feast (fēst), NOUN. a big meal for some special occasion and for a number of guests; banquet: *We went to the wedding feast.*

flight (flīt), NOUN. a trip in an aircraft: *We had an enjoyable flight.*

excitement

flush (flush), VERB. to blush; glow: *Her face flushed when they laughed at her.* ❑ VERB **flush·es, flushed, flush·ing.**

France (frans), NOUN. a large country in western Europe.

G g

globe (glōb), NOUN. the Earth; world.

grain (grān), NOUN. one of the tiny bits of which sand, sugar, or salt is made up.

greed·y (grē′dē), ADJECTIVE. wanting more than your share of something: *The dictator was greedy for power and money.* ❑ ADJECTIVE **greed·i·er, greed·i·est.**

guest (gest), NOUN. a person who is received and entertained at someone else's home, club, and so on; visitor.

guest

H h

howl (houl), VERB. to give a long, loud, sad cry: *Our dog often can be heard howling at night.* ❑ VERB **howls, howled, howl·ing.**

howl

hurl (hėrl), VERB. to throw something with great force: *She hurled a stone into the river.* ❑ VERB **hurls, hurled, hurl·ing.**

I i

in·stru·ment (in′strə mənt), NOUN. a device for measuring, recording, or controlling something. Rulers and yardsticks are instruments for measuring distance.

a hat	ė term	ô order	ch child	ə { a in about
ā age	i it	oi oil	ng long	e in taken
ä far	ī ice	ou out	sh she	i in pencil
â care	o hot	u cup	th thin	o in lemon
e let	ō open	ù put	ᵮн then	u in circus
ē equal	ò saw	ü rule	zh measure	

Ll

la·bel (lā′bəl), NOUN. a piece of paper or cloth that is sewed, glued, or fastened to something. A label tells what something is, who it belongs to, or who made it.

launch (lȯnch), VERB. to send something out into the air with force: *They will launch the satellite in a rocket.* ❑ VERB **launch·es, launched, launch·ing.**

launch

learn (lėrn), VERB. to gain knowledge or skill: *We are learning a lot at school.* ❑ VERB **learns, learned, learn·ing.**

ledge (lej), NOUN. a narrow shelf: *My cat loves to sit on the window ledge.*

light·ning (līt′ning), NOUN. a flash of electricity in the sky. The sound that it makes is thunder.

luck·y (luk′ē), ADJECTIVE. having or bringing good luck: *I think I am a very lucky person. My team always wins when I wear my lucky hat.* ❑ ADJECTIVE **luck·i·er, luck·i·est.**

Mm

mag·ic (maj′ik), NOUN.
1 the skill of seeming to make things appear, disappear, or change into something else; performing tricks that seem to be impossible: *The magician made rabbits appear out of the hat by magic.*
2 something that produces results as if by magic; mysterious influence; unexplained power: *The magic of music made us feel rested and happy.*

magic

mail (māl), VERB. to send by way of the post office; put in a mailbox: *I am mailing a letter to you.* ❑ VERB **mails, mailed, mail·ing.**

meas·ure (mezh′ər), VERB. to find the size or amount of something; find how long, wide, deep, large, or much something is: *We measured the amount of water in the pail and found that it was two liters.* ❑ VERB **meas·ures, meas·ured, meas·ur·ing.**

mon·soon (mon sün′), NOUN.
1 a powerful wind of the Indian Ocean and southern Asia. It blows from the southwest from April to October and from the northeast during the rest of the year.
2 a season during which this wind blows from the southwest, usually bringing heavy rains.

N n

nest (nest), NOUN. a kind of home that birds build out of twigs, leaves, mud, and the like. Birds lay their eggs and protect their young ones in nests.

nest

news·pa·per (nüz′pā′pər), NOUN. sheets of paper printed every day or week, telling the news and carrying advertisements, pictures, articles, and useful information.

P p

pal·ace (pal′is), NOUN. a very large, grand house, especially the official home of a king or queen.

a	hat	ė	term	ô	order	ch	child	⎰a in about
ā	age	i	it	oi	oil	ng	long	⎪e in taken
ä	far	ī	ice	ou	out	sh	she	ə ⎨i in pencil
â	care	o	hot	u	cup	th	thin	⎪o in lemon
e	let	ō	open	u̇	put	ŦH	then	⎱u in circus
ē	equal	ȯ	saw	ü	rule	zh	measure	

paste (pāst), NOUN. a mixture you use to stick things together. It is often made of flour and water boiled together.

pre·cip·i·ta·tion (pri sip′ə tā′shən), NOUN. the water that falls to the Earth in the form of rain, snow, sleet, or hail: *The forecast calls for some precipitation this afternoon.*

pasture

pas·ture (pas′chər), NOUN. a grassy field where cattle, sheep, or horses can feed.

po·ny (pō′nē), NOUN. a kind of small horse. Ponies are usually less than 5 feet tall at the shoulder. ❏ PLURAL **po·nies.**

pool (pül), NOUN. a small pond: *There were frogs around the forest pool.*

pro·nounce (prə nouns′), VERB. to say or make the sounds of a word; speak: *He pronounced that word differently than I did.* ❏ VERB **pro·nounc·es, pro·nounced, pro·nounc·ing.**

R r

rec·i·pe (res′ə pē), NOUN. a set of written directions that show you how to fix something to eat: *Please give me your recipe for bread.* ❏ PLURAL **rec·i·pes.**

re·frig·e·ra·tor (ri frij′ə rā′tər), NOUN. an electrical appliance that keeps food or other things cold; fridge.

ref·uge (ref′yüj), NOUN. shelter or protection from danger or trouble.

re·mark·a·ble (ri mär′kə bəl), ADJECTIVE. worth noticing because it is unusual: *He has a remarkable memory for names and faces.*

re·spect (ri spekt′), NOUN. a feeling of honor and admiration: *The children show great respect for their parents.*

respect

re·ward (ri wôrd′), NOUN. something you get in return for something that you have done: *A summer at camp was her reward for high grades.*

route (rüt *or* rout), NOUN. a way that you choose to get somewhere: *Will you go to the coast by the northern route?*

rus·tle (rus′əl),
1 NOUN. a light, soft sound of things gently rubbing together: *The breeze caused rustling of the leaves.*
2 VERB. to make or cause to make this sound: *The leaves rustled in the wind.*
3 ADJECTIVE. making this sound: *I love the sound of rustling leaves.*
❏ VERB **rus·tles, rus·tled, rus·tling.**

S s

sad·dle (sad′l), NOUN. a seat for a rider on a horse's back, or on a bicycle or motorcycle.

sauce (sȯs), NOUN. something, usually a liquid, served with or on food to make it taste better.

a	hat	ė	term	ô	order	ch	child		a in about
ā	age	i	it	oi	oil	ng	long		e in taken
ä	far	ī	ice	ou	out	sh	she	ə	i in pencil
â	care	o	hot	u	cup	th	thin		o in lemon
e	let	ō	open	ů	put	ŦH	then		u in circus
ē	equal	ȯ	saw	ü	rule	zh	measure		

soar

scold (skōld), VERB. to speak to someone in an angry way: *She scolded the kids for making such a mess.* ❑ VERB **scolds, scold•ed, scold•ing.**

scout (skout), NOUN. someone who is sent out to get information: *The leader of the expedition sent a scout ahead of the group to look for water.*

shone (shōn), VERB. a past tense of **shine:** *The sun shone all last week.*

sin•gle (sing′gəl), ADJECTIVE. only one: *The spider hung by a single thread.*

snatch (snach), VERB. to seize something suddenly: *The hawk snatched the fish and flew away.* ❑ VERB **snatch•es, snatched, snatch•ing.**

soar (sôr), VERB. to fly at a great height; fly upward: *The eagle soars without flapping its wings.* ❑ VERB **soars, soared, soar•ing.** ■ Another word that sounds like this is **sore.**

sore (sôr), NOUN. a painful place on your body where the skin or flesh is broken or bruised. ■ Another word that sounds like this is **soar.**

spar•kling (spär′kling), ADJECTIVE. shining; glittering: *Sparkling stars filled the night sky.*

sparkling

spied (spīd), VERB. the past participle of **spy:** *Who has spied on us?*

splash (splash), VERB. to cause water or another liquid to fly about and get people wet or dirty: *The swimmers like to splash each other with water.*
❑ VERB **splash•es, splashed, splash•ing.**

splash

spring (spring), NOUN. the season when plants begin to grow; season of the year between winter and summer.

star•tle (stär′tl), VERB. to frighten someone suddenly; surprise: *The dog jumped at the girl and startled her.*
❑ VERB **star•tles, star•tled, star•tling.**

sta•tion (stā′shən), NOUN.
1 a regular stopping place along a route: *We'll get off at the next train station.*
2 a building or place used for a special reason: *The suspect was taken to the police station.*

stom•ach (stum′ək), NOUN. the large muscular bag in the body which receives food that is swallowed. The stomach digests some food before passing it on to the intestines.

stum•ble (stum′bəl), VERB. to walk in an unsteady way: *As the tired hikers began to stumble, they knew it was time to rest.* ❑ VERB **stum•bles, stum•bled, stum•bling.**

startle

a	hat	ė	term	ô	order	ch	child		a in about
ā	age	i	it	oi	oil	ng	long		e in taken
ä	far	ī	ice	ou	out	sh	she	ə	i in pencil
â	care	o	hot	u	cup	th	thin		o in lemon
e	let	ō	open	ù	put	ᴛʜ	then		u in circus
ē	equal	ȯ	saw	ü	rule	zh	measure		

stur·dy (stėr′dē), ADJECTIVE. strong:
She was a very sturdy child.
❑ ADJECTIVE **stur·di·er, stur·di·est.**
–stur′di·ly, ADVERB.

sub·trop·i·cal (sub trop′ə kəl),
ADJECTIVE. bordering on the tropics;
nearly tropical.

suc·cess (sək ses′), NOUN. a result that
you hoped and planned for: *Success
in school comes from intelligence and
hard work.* ❑ PLURAL **suc·cess·es.**

swan (swän), NOUN. a large, graceful
water bird with a long, slender,
curving neck. Adult swans are usually
pure white.

swan

swift (swift), ADJECTIVE. moving very fast;
able to move very fast: *The cowboy
needed a swift horse.*

T t

tail (tāl), NOUN. the part that sticks out
from the back of an animal's body.
Rabbits have short tails. Mice have
long tails. ■ Another word that
sounds like this is **tale.**

tale (tāl), NOUN. a story, either made-up
or true: *We always enjoy hearing
Grandfather's tales of his boyhood.*
■ Another word that sounds like this
is **tail.**

thief (thēf), NOUN. someone who steals
something: *A thief stole my bicycle from
the yard.* ❑ PLURAL **thieves** (thēvs).

thirst (therst), NOUN. a dry, uncomfortable feeling in the mouth or throat caused by a need to have a drink: *She satisfied her thirst with a glass of water.*

thun•der (thun′dər), NOUN. the loud noise from the sky that comes after a flash of lightning. It is caused by a disturbance of the air resulting from the discharge of electricity.

treas•ure (trezh′ər), NOUN. valuable things, such as gold and jewels: *The pirates buried treasure along the coast.*

trop•i•cal (trop′ə kəl), ADJECTIVE. of or like the regions of the Earth near the equator: *Bananas are tropical fruit.*

U u

un•u•su•al (un yü′zhü əl), ADJECTIVE. not in common use; uncommon; rare: *Blue is an unusual color for food.* **–un•u′su•al•ly,** ADVERB.

W w

weath•er (weᴛʜ′ər), NOUN. the conditions of the air outside at a certain place and time. Weather includes facts about temperature, wind, sun, rainfall, and so on.

weigh (wā), VERB. to have as a weight of: *I weighed 110 pounds last year.* ❏ VERB **weighs, weighed, weigh•ing.**

whip (wip), VERB. to move, put, or pull something quickly and suddenly: *She whipped off her coat.* ❏ VERB **whips, whipped, whip•ping.**

unusual

a	hat	ė	term	ô	order	ch	child		a in about
ā	age	i	it	oi	oil	ng	long		e in taken
ä	far	ī	ice	ou	out	sh	she	ə	i in pencil
â	care	o	hot	u	cup	th	thin		o in lemon
e	let	ō	open	ù	put	ᴛʜ	then		u in circus
ē	equal	ò	saw	ü	rule	zh	measure		

whirl (wėrl), VERB. to turn or swing round and round very fast; spin: *The leaves whirled in the wind.*
❏ VERB **whirls, whirled, whirl·ing.**

whirl

wind¹ (wind), NOUN. air that is moving. The wind varies in force from a slight breeze to a strong gale.

wind² (wīnd), VERB. to move this way and that; change direction; turn: *A brook winds through the woods.*
❏ VERB **winds, wound, wind·ing.**

World War I (wėrld wôr wun), a war fought from 1914 to 1918. The United States, Great Britain, France, Russia, and their allies were on one side; Germany, Austria-Hungary, and their allies were on the other side.

a	hat	ė	term	ô	order	ch	child		a in about
ā	age	i	it	oi	oil	ng	long		e in taken
ä	far	ī	ice	ou	out	sh	she	ə	i in pencil
â	care	o	hot	u	cup	th	thin		o in lemon
e	let	ō	open	ù	put	ŦH	then		u in circus
ē	equal	ò	saw	ü	rule	zh	measure		

Acknowledgments

Text

Page 12: From *Doctor Coyote* retold by John Bierhorst. Text copyright © 1987 by John Bierhorst. Reprinted by permission of Simon & Schuster Books for Young Readers, an imprint of Simon & Schuster Children's Publishing Division.

Page 14: From *Ananse's Feast* by Tololwa M. Mollel. Text copyright © 1997 by Tololwa M. Mollel. Illustrations copyright © 1997 by Andrew Glass. All rights reserved. Reprinted by permission of Clarion Books/Houghton Mifflin Company.

Page 34: "The Fox and the Stork" from *Fifty Fabulous Fables* by Suzanne I. Barchers. Copyright © 1997 Suzanne I. Barchers. All rights reserved. Reprinted by permission of Teacher Ideas Press, A Division of Libraries Unlimited, Inc.

Page 38: From *The Lost Lake* by Allen Say. Copyright © 1989 by Allen Say. All rights reserved. Reprinted by permission of Houghton Mifflin Company.

Page 40: *Sam and the Lucky Money* by Karen Chinn. Illustrated by Cornelius Van Wright & Ying-Hwa Hu. Text copyright © 1995 by Karen Chinn. Illustrations copyright © 1995 by Cornelius Van Wright and Ying-Hwa Hu. Reprinted by permission of Lee & Low Books, Inc.

Page 60: From *Fire!* by Caroline Evans. Copyright © 1995 by the National Wildlife Federation. Reprinted from the October 1995 issue of *Ranger Rick Magazine* with the permission of the publisher, the National Wildlife Federation.

Page 62: *Thunder Cake* by Patricia Polacco. Copyright © 1990 by Babushka, Inc. Reprinted by permission of Philomel Books, a division of Penguin Putnam, Inc.

Page 84: Excerpt from *Darkness and the Butterfly* by Ann Grifalconi, 1987, pp. 1–6. Copyright © 1987 by Ann Grifalconi. Reprinted by permission of Little, Brown and Company.

Page 86: *One Grain of Rice: A Mathematical Folktale* by Demi. Published by Scholastic Press, a division of Scholastic, Inc. Copyright © 1997 by Demi. Reprinted by permission of Scholastic, Inc.

Page 109: From *Rice* by Lynne Merrison. Illustrated by John Yates. Copyright © 1990 by Carolrhoda Books, Inc. All rights reserved. Reprinted by permission of the publisher.

Page 112: From *Uncle Nacho's Hat* adapted by Harriet Rohmer. Copyright © 1998 by Harriet Rohmer. Reprinted with permission of the publisher, Children's Book Press, San Francisco, CA.

Page 114: *The Woman Who Outshone the Sun* by Alejandro Cruz Martinez. Text copyright © 1991 by Children's Book Press and Rosalma Zubizarreta. Pictures copyright © 1991 by Fernando Olivera. Reprinted with permission of the publisher, Children's Book Press, San Francisco, CA.

Page 132: *Going Through the Old Photos* by Michael Rosen. Copyright © 1979 by Michael Rosen. Reprinted by permission of The Peters Fraser and Dunlop Group Limited on behalf of Michael Rosen.

Page 133: "Quilt" from *A Suitcase of Seaweed* by Janet S. Wong. Copyright © 1996 Janet S. Wong. Reprinted by permission of Margaret K. McElderry Books, an imprint of Simon & Schuster Children's Publishing Division.

Page 134: "The Stars/Las estrellas" by Nelly Palacio Jaramillo. Text copyright © 1994 by Nelly Palacio Jaramillo. Translation © 1994 by Raquel Jaramillo. Reprinted by permission of Henry Holt and Company, Inc.

Page 135: "Sky Bear" from *The Earth Under Sky Bear's Feet* by Joseph Bruchac, 1995. Copyright © by Joseph Bruchac. Reprinted by permission of Penguin Putnam, Inc.

Page 138: From *Grandpa Is a Flyer* by Sanna Anderson Baker. Text copyright © 1995 by Sanna Anderson Baker. Excerpt reprinted by permission of Albert Whitman & Company.

Page 140: *Flight: The Journey of Charles Lindbergh* by Robert Burleigh. Text copyright © 1991 by Robert Burleigh. Illustrations copyright © 1991 by Mike Wimmer. Reprinted by permission of Philomel Books, a division of Penguin Putnam, Inc.

Page 162: From "Moving Along on Bike Trails" by Stewart Warren, *The Herald News,* August 5, 1998. Reprinted by permission of *The Herald News,* Joliet, IL.

Page 164: Chapter One from *Chibi: A True Story from Japan* by Barbara Brenner and Julia Takaya. Text copyright © 1996 by Barbara Brenner and Julia Takaya. Illustrations copyright © 1996 by June Otani. All rights reserved. Reprinted by permission of Clarion Books/Houghton Mifflin Company.

Page 186: From *A Little Excitement* by Marc Harshman. Text copyright © 1989 by Marc Harshman. Reprinted by permission of Cobblehill Books, an affiliate of Dutton Children's Books, a division of Penguin Putnam, Inc.

Page 188: *Brave Irene* by William Steig. Copyright © 1986 by William Steig. Reprinted by permission of Farrar, Straus & Giroux, Inc.

Page 209: "Water on Earth" by David Heil et al. From *Discover the Wonder.* Copyright © 1996 Scott, Foresman and Company, Glenview, Illinois.

Page 212: From *Tomás and the Library Lady* by Pat Mora. Text copyright © 1997 by Pat Mora. Reprinted by permission of Random House, Inc.

Page 214: From *More Than Anything Else* by Marie Bradby. Illustrated by Chris K. Soentpiet. Text copyright © 1995 by Marie Bradby. Illustrations copyright © 1995 by Chris K. Soentpiet. Reprinted by permission of Orchard Books, New York.

Page 232: Excerpt from *Popsicle Pony* by Jill Stover, 1994, pp 1–8. Copyright © 1994 by Jill Stover. Reprinted by permission of William Morrow & Company.

Page 234: *Leah's Pony* by Elizabeth Friedrich. Illustrated by Michael Garland. Text copyright © 1996 by Elizabeth Friedrich. Illustrations copyright © by Michael Garland. All rights reserved. Reprinted by permission of Boys Mills Press, Inc.

Page 252: "At the Library" from *It's Raining Laughter* by Nikki Grimes. Copyright © 1997 by Nikki Grimes. Reprinted by permission of Dial Books for Young Readers, a division of Penguin Putnam, Inc.

Page 252: "A Book" from *My Head Is Red and Other Riddle Rhymes* by Myra Cohn Livingston. Copyright © 1990 by Myra Cohn Livingston. Reprinted by permission of Marian Reiner.

Page 253: "Somewhere" from *Is Somewhere Always Far Away?* by Leland B. Jacobs. Copyright © 1993 by Allan D. Jacobs. Reprinted by permission of Henry Holt and Company, Inc.

Page 254: "Let's send a rocket" from *Poems to Me* by Kit Patrickson. © 1978 by Ginn and Company, reprinted by permission of Silver Burdett Ginn.

Page 255: "The Moon, a Banana" by Jesús Carlos Soto Morfín. English version translated by Judith Infante. Translation © copyright Judith Infante. Reprinted by permission of Judith Infante.

Page 258: From *Tate Gallery Drawing: A Young Artist's Guide* by Jude Welton. Copyright © 1994 Dorling Kindersley Limited, London. Text copyright © 1994 Jude Welton. Reprinted by permission of Dorling Kindersley, New York.

Page 260: Excerpts adapted from *The Piñata Maker/El Piñatero* by George Ancona. Copyright © 1994 by George Ancona. Reprinted by permission of Harcourt Brace & Company.

Page 275: "Southwest Settlements" from *Social Studies Communities Around Us* by J.R. Garcia, D.J. Gelo, L.L. Greenow, K.B. Kracht, D.G. White. © 1997 by Silver Burdett Ginn, Simon & Schuster Education Group. Used by permission.

Page 278: Excerpt from *Bonanza Girl* by Patricia Beatty, pp. 16 & 17. Copyright © 1962 by Patricia Beatty. Reprinted by permission of William Morrow & Company.

Page 280: *Mailing May* by Michael O. Tunnell. Text copyright © 1997 by Michael O. Tunnell. Illustration copyright © 1997 by Ted Rand. Reprinted by permission of Tambourine Books and Greenwillow Books, division of William Morrow & Company, Inc.